The beautiful and simple Durham Miners' Memorial in Durham Cathedral, quotes a passage from the book of Job: "They are forgotten of the foot that passeth." This writer hopes that this little effort will help to ensure that the 76 men and boys who perished in the Clay Cross Calamities, and the hundreds of others who died less publicised but no less tragic deaths over the long history of Derbyshire's coalmining industry, are never forgotten.

Frontispiece courtesy of Mr. G. Sparham

In Affectionate Remembrance

OF

THE 45 MEN AND BOYS,

Who lost their lives by the Explosion in the No. 7 Pit, Danesmoor, belonging to the Clay Cross Company, November 7th, 1882.

BAKER, Phineas, Single, Aged 53 Years.
BARKER, Samuel, Married, Aged 42 Years.
BARKER, Edward, (Son of above) Aged 15 Years.
BEESON, Henry, Married, Aged 44 Years.
BEESON, Aaron,   Sons of   Single, Aged 23 Years.
BEESON, John,   Henry Beeson   Aged 14 Years.
BERRY, Thomas, Married, Aged 34 Years.
BIRKIN, Thomas, Married, Aged 38 Years.
BOWLER, Elias, Married, Aged 34 Years.
BRIGGS, William, Married, Aged 29 Years.
BUCKBERRY, John, Married, Aged 37 Years.
CHAPPELL, Thomas, Single, Aged 22 Years.
CLARK, Emanuel, Married, Aged 42 Years.
CLARK, William, Single, (Son of the above) Aged 21 Years.
DUNN, Joseph,   Married, Aged 24 Years.
DUNN, William,   Brothers   Aged 16 Years.
DUNN, Richard, Married, (Uncle of the above) Aged 37 Years.
EDWARDS, James, Married, Aged 32 Years.
FOWLER, John, Married, Aged 48 Years.
GOALEY, Thomas, Married, Aged 25 Years.
HEWITT, George, Widower, Aged 46 Years.
HEWITT, Thomas,   Sons of   Single, Aged 23 Years.
HEWITT, Joseph,   George Hewitt   Single, Aged 21 Years.
HOLMES, John, Married, Aged 50 Years.
MARTIN, William Henry, Single, Aged 21 Years.
MITCHELL, George, Married, Aged 45 Years.
PARKER, James, Married, Aged 25 Years.
PARKIN, Michael, Married, Aged 47 Years.
PHIPPS, Joseph, Married, Aged 47 Years.
RENSHAW, William, Married, Aged 36 Years.
RICHARDS, Owen, Married, Aged 36 Years.
SCOTHERN, Philip, Married, Aged 47 Years.
SHELTON, William, Single, Aged 21 Years.
SIMS, James, Married, Aged 45 Years.
SLINN, William, Married, Aged 37 Years.
SMITH, James, Married, Aged 32 Years.
SQUIRES, William, Single, Aged 35 Years.
STANLEY, John, Married, Aged 45 Years.
STONE, Joseph, (No. 1)   Twin   Married, Aged 35 Years.
STONE, Jacob,   Brothers   Married, Aged 35 Years.
STONE, Joseph, (No. 2) Married, Aged 50 Years.
TAYLOR, Richard, (No. 1) Married, Aged 30 Years.
TAYLOR, Richard, (No. 2) Married, Aged 25 Years.
VICKERS, William, Single, Aged 20 Years.
WALTERS, Joseph, Married, Aged 27 Years.

Say not, they passed from life to death.
Their day was night, and night was day,
Where earth's black darkness held its sway ; and this to cease
Was passing up from death to life,
Where night is day,—day without night ;
In everlasting heaven'ly light, to rest in peace.

WILLIAM JOHNSON, Printer, Clay Cross.

THE
CLAY CROSS CALAMITIES

by

Terry Judge

Scarthin Books
1994

ACKNOWLEDGEMENTS

A number of people have helped bring this book from a jumble of notes to its present form, to whom I owe my thanks: the late Mr James Simms and Mr Earnest Walker; Mr Dick Childs, Cliff Williams and John Robinson; the staff of the Chesterfield Local Studies Library, and in particular Mrs Jean Radford of the Matlock Local Studies Library who convinced me to write it; Mr George Sparham for help with the plans; John Currey of Seaham, County Durham for use of his photographs; Mr Russ Draycott of Sutton in Ashfield for his photographs.

My publishers, Scarthin Books, for their faith. My Editor Dr David Mitchell for his patience and tolerance, he needed, and has, much of both. Pamela Hopkinson for all her valued help. My wife Janice and daughter Fiona who supplied endless cups of tea, swept up numerous fag-ends and were never-ever critical!

If a dedication is appropriate to this little work then it is to the thousands of men who worked in the coal and iron-stone mines in the County of Derby; I am proud to have been one of that number.

Terry Judge, Bolsover, 1994.

Terry Judge was born in Heage, Derbyshire, and has spent most of his life in deep mining or opencast mining. His interests are geology and local history, particularly mining history, and he is the the secretary of Highedge Historical Society. Terry lives in Bolsover and is married with three sons and a daughter. He is working on a further book of mining history.

Published 1994 by Scarthin Books, Cromford, Derbyshire

© Terry Judge 1994

Phototypesetting by Paragon Typesetters

Printed by Redwood Books

ISBN 0 907758 79 7

CONTENTS

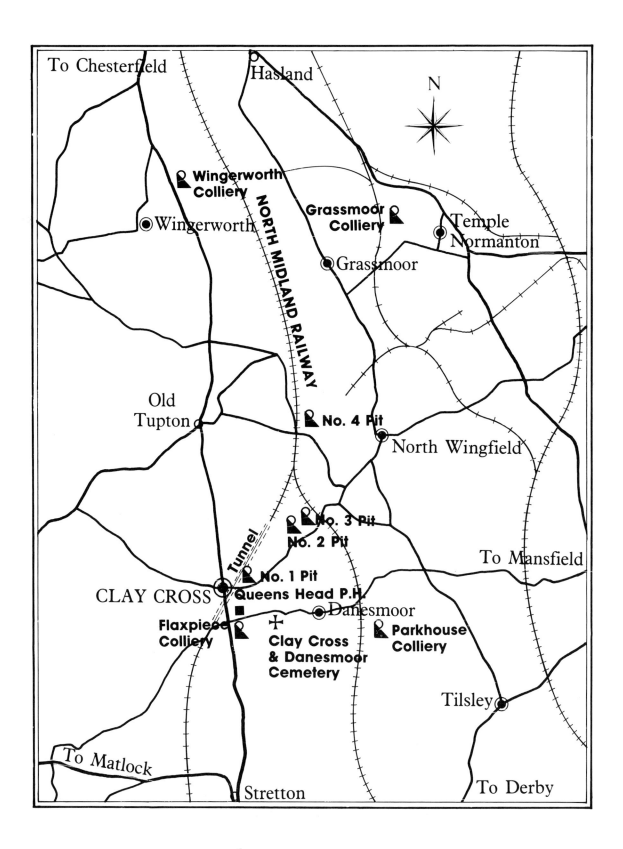

To Chesterfield

Hasland

N

Wingerworth Colliery

Grassmoor Colliery

Temple Normanton

Wingerworth

NORTH MIDLAND RAILWAY

Grassmoor

Old Tupton

No. 4 Pit

North Wingfield

No. 3 Pit

No. 2 Pit

Tunnel

To Mansfield

No. 1 Pit

CLAY CROSS

Queens Head P.H.

Danesmoor

Parkhouse Colliery

Flaxpiece Colliery

Clay Cross & Danesmoor Cemetery

Tilsley

To Matlock

Stretton

To Derby

Chapter 1

A Mining Story

The little graveyard of St Luke's Church, Heage contains the last, often unmarked, resting place of many coal miners. Some lived out their normal span whilst others, as some stones testify, were not so fortunate. The stones themselves are a part of the history of the village, they record the names of pits now half-forgotten, their visible remains long ago wiped away, their plans stored in dusty archives or in many cases never recorded at all. Denby Hall, Hartshay, Heage Bond-Londe, Heage Norton, Morley Park, Salterwood, Calley, Denby Colliery and dozens of other local mines have at different times given employment to the men of Heage, and some pits far distant from the village have also claimed its sons. In 1993 only two miners actually lived in the village; one worked in Nottinghamshire, and the other, my brother, went even further, to Coventry Colliery to follow his calling.

Miners have always been prepared to move around the coalfields in search of work; stoppages, strikes, blacklists, exhaustion of pits, or even plain restlessness providing the catalyst. The opening of a new colliery with all its glittering promise of hope and dreams fulfilled, must always have had a strong appeal to the men employed in old, badly ventilated pits, with worn out equipment, the best of their coal seams exhausted. Because of the location of many new 19th century mines away from existing towns and villages, owners were forced to provide new housing far superior to anything the average miner had experienced before. Higher earnings in pits with thick, untouched seams closer to the pit bottom; the provision of newer technology; supervision by managements directly employed by the owner (rather than the butty system where a contractor took on the responsibility for the under-ground work and its supervision) – all were important factors in determining a man to 'up sticks' and move out of the village to work in a new pit. In most cases, however, he was not much better off. He exchanged a run-down, perhaps centuries-old cottage for a new, but jerry-built house, with far more rules and conditions than his previous landlord could have imposed. Short booms when work was plentiful still turned all too quickly into the same lay-offs and stoppages that had plagued his earlier life. The village was new, but the pawn shop, the tommy shop, the servility to the new-style Gaffer remained part of the miners' daily life.

Three such men, James Simms, Joseph Stone and Elias Bowler, at some time in the latter half of the 19th century, perhaps around 1874, left the Heage pits and took their families to Clay Cross.

All three men are known to have been previously employed at the Morley Park Works (the remains of which still stand beside the A38 Ripley by-pass, stark, gaunt reminders of a bygone age), where former generations of their families had laboured both above and below ground. They were not the only ones to make the move, many family names in Clay Cross and Danesmoor can still be traced back today from the Heage, Belper, and Ripley areas.

The Morley Park Works by 1874 were in a parlous state. Almost twenty years of internecine warfare between members of the lessee's family, followed by more troubles with the owner, resulted in bankruptcy, rundown plant and neglect, only for the new lessee to then die in a tragic accident, falling from his horse. All this may have gone some way to enforcing the moves. Whatever the reason, by 1882 the men were settled in North Derbyshire and were at work in Parkhouse pit, a modern colliery belonging to the Clay Cross Company. They are buried together in a single grave in Heage churchyard, which, perhaps, is as it should be. They were workmates, lifelong friends, and two of them were brothers-in-law. How did they die; why were they buried together, and why were they taken back to the village of their birth? The answers to the questions lie a few miles to the north of Heage, just inside the gate of Clay Cross and Danesmoor cemetery, where a weeping angel hangs her head over stone tablets recording the names of these and others of their workmates who died in Clay Cross No. 7 pit, Parkhouse, in November 1882.

The public talk of the cost of coal in purely monetary terms, the miner on the other hand speaks of *the cost of coal* [author's italic] in an entirely different way. His costs are paid in blood, sweat, blue-scarred heads and bodies, and his

The gravestone in St Luke's churchyard Heage. Cleaned and re-erected 1994

receipts are recorded on gravestones the length and breadth of the coalfields.

There is nothing remarkable about a gravestone which records a mining death, walk through the churchyard in any Derbyshire mining village and you will find them, why should this particular one in a remote, almost forgotten village be any different? But it is different, special because it calls to mind great events, important events which even now, over a hundred years on; help to show the outsider that the miner is special, why he has a bond with his fellows, that those who view him from outside cannot begin to share or understand. The railway that in the beginning shaped Clay Cross, the man whose vision brought the railway, sank the pits and built a works that survive to this day; the greatest loss of life from explosion in any Derbyshire colliery – all have their part in the story of that little slab of limestone, and, simply, inadequately, this is their story.

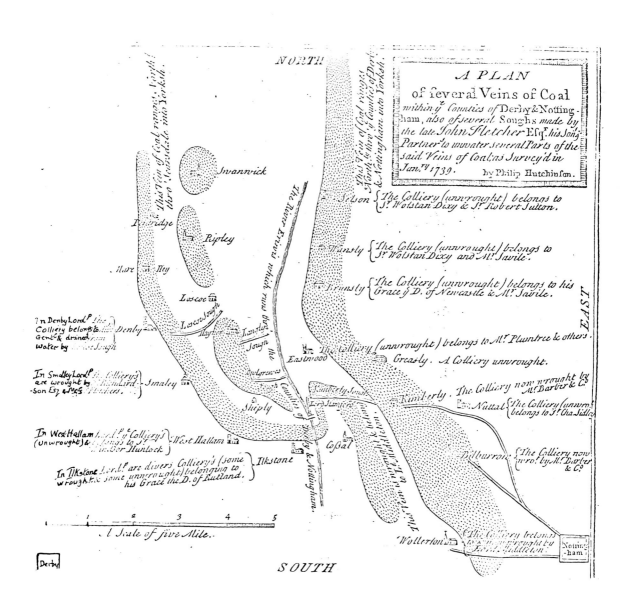

An early mineral plan showing the outcrop of the Top Hard and Deep Hard seams over an extensive area.

10

Chapter 2

THE DERBYSHIRE COALFIELD, ITS DANGERS AND DEVELOPMENT

Geologically the Derbyshire Coalfield is some 250-300 million years old. Formed in a huge, slowly subsiding delta during what geologists term the Carboniferous Age, the coal measures are a mixture of shales, sandstones, mudstones and coalseams with many interbedded layers (termed rakes) of ironstone. The coal measures overlie millstone grit, which in turn overlies limestone, together the whole sequence of rocks is knows as the Carboniferous.

Aeons ago this whole series of rocks were tilted, contorted, faulted and partly eroded until they resembled their present state. Sometimes, due to one or other of the above circumstances, rocks show on the surface where they can be easily worked. When this happens they are said to outcrop, or basset.

Faulting often throws rocks to the surface – a fortuitous faulting brings the limestone of Crich and Ashover against the coalfield – and faults sometimes aided the miner when he began to venture beneath the surface of the ground. Sandstone is porous, where it shows at outcrop this porosity enables vast quantities of water to percolate underground. Because the shales and mudstones are impervious to water, it lies trapped within the sandstone. Faulting can bring these dangerous underground springs within reach of workings and ordinary working practices can then enable water to enter a mine.

Coal was formed from decaying vegetable matter. Because this matter was in many cases buried very quickly, the gases given off during the distillation and conversion into a bituminous state were trapped, either within the seams themselves or if overlain with sandstone within its microscopic pores. Some seams contain huge amounts of gas, and before the miner fully understood its nature, he termed such seams 'fiery'.

Coal forms only a very small percentage of the rocks within the coal measures and the seams vary greatly in thickness, quality and content. Not all coal is the same; some is good house-coal, steam coal, coking and furnace grade. Rarely, some of these properties are contained within just one seam and different portions will be worked independently.

Coal dust itself is explosive, usually with devastating force; many coal dust explosions have occurred in Derbyshire pits, but usually with only small loss of life compared to similar happenings in other areas. The effect of a coal dust explosion is often more violent than one composed from gas; luck has played its part in the past that death tolls from coal dust explosions have not been far higher in Derbyshire.

The gas given off by coal seams is methane, a gas which is odourless, colourless and cannot be detected by taste. Lighter in the air, its greatest danger to the miner is that when mixed with oxygen within certain ranges of combustion it becomes highly explosive. The miner terms this

A swamp in the Caboniferous Age, some 300 million years ago.

gas firedamp and it is an ever present force that he has had to learn to live with and respect.

Damp is a general term used by miners to define gases. It is related to the German term for gas, *dampf* (perhaps a survival even of an early Anglo/Danish term? Coal was certainly mined during the 9th century and the Normans and Angevin clerics often referred to *le dampf*). When an explosion of methane or coal dust occurs underground a mixture of gases is derived from the ensuing combustion which the miner calls afterdamp. Afterdamp is usually a mixture of carbon monoxide and carbon dioxide, will not support life, has no physical violence and is usually found in mines in association with whitedamp (carbon monoxide). Nearly as heavy as air, afterdamp causes violent headaches and is extremely dangerous, it is the reason that canaries were carried underground after explosions as their respiratory systems are affected by this gas long before a man would show any signs.

Blackdamp, sometimes called stythe, will also be met in this story. It is a mixture of carbon dioxide and nitrogen and will not support life or flame. Found always in old workings and unventilated parts of the mine, heavier than air, it puts out miners' flame-safety lamps and kills by swift suffocation. Another name for it is chokedamp. These gases all play a large part in the story of Clay Cross.

It is not recorded when the first Derbyshire man began to dig for coal. Indeed it is almost certain that he was not a Derbyshire man at all! He may well have been a Celt, Roman, Mercian or Northumbrian, Angle or Dane, long before the shire was formed. It is certain that by the time the Normans began keeping records, mining in the county was becoming widespread, whether for iron ore or coal is difficult to distinguish, but it is virtually impossible to recover one without at least coming into contact with the other.

King Henry II declared the area between the rivers Derwent and Erewash to be forest, this covers almost the entire exposed coalfield south of Chesterfield to its boundary near Little Eaton, just north of Derby. Twelfth and 13th century grants, fees and fines, and a wealth of manorial records, make clear the fact that mining was allowed, albeit on a very small scale.

Careful observation of workings uncovered by opencast mining has shown that where ironstone pits are known to have been worked (from documentary research), and where those pits have passed through coalseams, the coal dug was not discarded or used as backfill but must have been used for some purpose.

Timber has always been a valuable commodity. Forest records for Duffield Frith and elsewhere in the county, make it clear that the forest trees were carefully husbanded, even the underwoods such as birch and hazel having specific uses. Alder seems to have been the preferred wood for charcoal making and it was always sold 'by commission', in other words by licence to one buyer. Commoners had rights to collect deadwood at certain times, but it seems obvious that in poor, agrarian communities, coal would have been a useful and welcome addition.

A Roman road (Ryknild Street) and a later, important turnpike road both link the towns of Chesterfield and Derby, crossing north to south over the middle coal-measures, the most productive portions of the coalfield. It seems significant that some of the early ironworks around the two main county towns were directly linked by these roads. Perhaps it was iron that first attracted the early miner?

Derbyshire is a landlocked county. Until the making of its early turnpikes around the end of the first quarter of the 18th century, its roads had changed little since early medieval times and were in a parlous state. It was not until the development of these, along with the canals, and later the railways; that the coal industry could grow and supply other than purely local markets.

Bell-Pit workings exposed by opencasting. Courtesy of Mr. Hugh Richmond.

Chapter 3

EARLY COALMINING METHODS

Medieval records show that much coal was worked under licence, termed 'farming', to small groups of persons – farmers. Thus in Morley Park, a Crown property after the succession of Henry, Duke of Lancaster to the throne of England, Richard le Milner and partners pay a farm-fee of £7 for the right to work sea coal (the term distinguishing mineral from charcoal), for the period, Michaelmas to Lady Day, 1443-44. This is a substantial sum for a farm of two picks, and suggests that coal mining was then of some importance. Richard's surname is of interest here as it implies that he was either a miner or miller. He could have been both; the area he was working was close to an early charcoal-fired furnace and the waterwheel that powered the bellows could well have powered a corn mill when the furnace was not in operation.

Bell-pits and openworks (delphs) appear to have been the preferred mining methods of the Middle Ages, but as the shallow workings along the outcrop of the main seams became exhausted, deeper, underground working had to follow and different techniques had to develop, particularly the vexing question of mine drainage. In Derbyshire, it is around early ironworks or close to the two main County towns that deeper mining seems to have developed first. Even these mines were relatively small-scale, and remained so until the building of the tall coke-fired furnaces of the late 18th century (like the existing ones at Morley Park).

It was furnaces like the ones at Morley Park and Wingerworth that began a new pattern of working coal mines. If the rapacious mouths were ever to be filled (and it was thought at the time that they should be kept in continuous operation for fear of damage if they were allowed to cool), then huge quantities of coal were needed. Coke-ovens, and increased production both in coal and ironstone mining were essential;

deeper mines with better use of available technology was the outcome.

If the pattern of working the mines at the Morley Park Works (begun in 1780) was similar in other areas, and there is good reason to suppose that it was, it is possible to say with some degree of accuracy what those methods were, as some of its working plans still exist.

An 18th Century coal mine, Morley Park, had similar surface arrangements. The Clay Cross pits were very different. Here pumping and winding are performed by the same central engine. Author's Collection.

It used to be said that a man could dig a hole in the early morning, strike coal before dinner time and recover his outlay by early afternoon. Over-simplified certainly; nevertheless pits such as that were sunk in many parts of the coalfield, even in the 20th century. Joseph Wright of Heage, along with his partner, sank just such a pit near Lower Hartshay in 1876. Using second-hand, but still useful, outdated tackle, working small areas of coal close to the surface and supplying a very local market at a few pence below the going rate of the bigger mines, they flourished for a few months and then passed into history, they were the remnants of the bell-pit era, the fossils of a bygone age. Worked and planned by practical colliers, they needed little supervision, were visited very infrequently by busy, harassed mines inspectors, they were usually left to their own devices and management.

Most of the early deep mines were planned and supervised by specialist mining engineers called viewers. The viewer was self-employed and was free to work for any number of coal owners at the same time. His methods became well tried and tested and as a viewer's reputation grew so his methods would more and more be adopted. Fletcher of Ripley, Boot of Somercotes, Campbell of Matlock and wider afield, Jonathan Woodhouse of Overseal, were to stamp their names as consultant mining engineers to numerous Derbyshire enterprises.

The existing plans for Morley Park show that although coal mining went deep underground, the ironstone was almost always recovered by means of bell-pits or openworks. No plan shows a specific ironstone pit with a shaft until late in the 19th century and even those are thought to be old, worked out coal pits. When the works closed and the plant and moveable assets were sold off, a poster specifies an "Ironstone Openwork" rather than a mine, the deep shafts all being termed "The Morley Park Collieries".

Pits such as Morley Park and Wingerworth were innovative, geared to a newer technology, but they were still of comparatively small scale compared with what was yet to come, they pointed the way forward, introduced cages, shaft guides, underground edge-rails, and adopted better mining methods, but by the time the railway came to Derbyshire their workings were old, their gear was worn out, and many of the prime seams were exhausted or unreachable by the existing pumping methods. It was time for the big pits to take over, King Coal had arrived in the county, riding on a coke-fired railway engine.

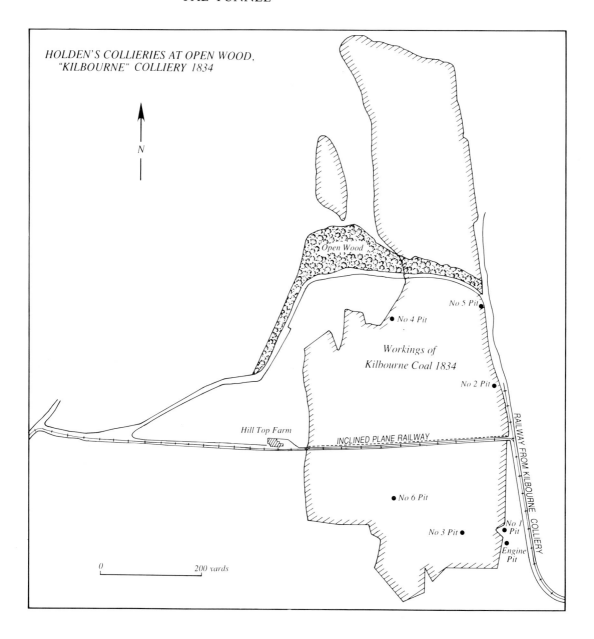

HOLDEN'S COLLIERIES AT OPEN WOOD,
"KILBOURNE" COLLIERY 1834

N

Open Wood

No 5 Pit

No 4 Pit

Workings of
Kilbourne Coal 1834

No 2 Pit

Hill Top Farm

INCLINED PLANE RAILWAY

RAILWAY FROM KILBOURNE COLLIERY

No 6 Pit

No 3 Pit

No 1
Pit

Engine
Pit

0   200 yards

*A number of
shafts sunk over
and into the line
of a Sough: Engine
pit, and No.'s 1,
2, 5. No.'s 4 and
6 are "Basset
Shafts". Author's
Collection.*

Chapter 4

THE TUNNEL

The story of George Stephenson's rise to fame needs no retelling. His life and times were held up as shining examples to every schoolchild and books telling of his deeds are still appearing today. Similarly the history of his involvement with the Midland Railway Company and how he came to found George Stephenson and Company at Clay Cross, is known, or should be, to every schoolchild. It is enough to record here, that his works, the railway which brought him here, his home at Tapton House, Chesterfield, and the village that his work created still survive. The tunnel which was in all probability his starting point can also be our own. (It is not intended that this work should give a detailed history of the tunnel, that has already been well-covered elsewhere. Anyone wishing to read an excellent account of its boring should read the book by my friend Cliff Williams *The Clay Cross Tunnel*, published by Scarthin Books.)

To this day, in the archives of the Clay Cross Company is a large-scale plan of the Clay Cross tunnel, which passes under the town to the north portal beside the works started by Stephenson. A glance at the plan shows that some of the most productive seams of the coal-measures were encountered during the boring.

Railway locomotives at the time were fired using coke for fuel and Stephenson was quick to realise that the blackshale seam through which the tunnel passed was ideal for coking purposes. (The historian of the Midland Railway, F.S. Williams, credits Stephenson with this discovery, also stating that "He traced the Blackshale outcrop northwards to Dronfield". In truth he did no such thing, the seam and its properties were already well known; pits had been mining the seam for years and its outcrop was traced years before the railway came.)

After a stormy two year passage through Parliament the

Railway Bill was eventually passed and work on the North Midland line began in 1837. At Clay Lane, then a small hamlet to the south of Chesterfield, a tunnel was required to take the line out of the Amber Valley through a hillside containing very wet coal-measures. Besides tunnelling from both ends, six working shafts were also sunk, enabling the engineers to have 14 working faces. These shafts, some of which later served as ventilation shafts for the tunnel and can still be seen today capped with iron grills, were worked in similar manner to many of the small mines of that period. Horse gins, a primitive winding arrangement driven by a horse walking in a circle to raise and lower the buckets, were used rather than more expensive steam engines. The railway historian tells that the spectacle of so many men at work day and night, with huge fires burning on the hilltop, became the great wonder of the surrounding countryside. The gangs of navvies, augmented as always by Stephenson's following of Northumbrian miners, quickly completed the 2,000 yard boring.

(Here again I feel that the railway historian has assumed too much, George Stephenson was not the contractor for the tunnel, that was in other hands. Stephenson had enough work of his own sinking and developing his colliery, to fully occupy his Northumbrians. It is very unlikely that any of them worked on the tunnel, indeed the plan referred to earlier shows miners working in the blackshale seam, presumably in headings [development roadways], preparing the pit. Perusal of the records of the names of miners employed in his first mine at Clay Cross, shows many names common to the Newcastle and Durham area. He was hardly likely to part with such skilled and faithful labour to help a contractor who, after all, was paying good wages for what was more of a navvying job than a mining skill.)

One factor among many which has made George Stephenson's name rank among the greats was the depth of his perception. He was always ready to grasp any opportunities which presented themselves as a result of his activities. At Clay Lane a unique set of circumstances came together and the engineer was quick to seize and develop them to great advantage.

The line required vast quantities of limestone, not only for mortar to be used in the great earthworks, but also for ballast on the roadbed. It has already been noticed that nature had brought the periclines of Crich and Ashover within sight of Clay Lane and also in close proximity to the line of the railway. By acquiring Crich quarry, easily reached by a cheap but efficient tramway and by building lime kilns near Ambergate this need was easily met. The Crich limestone is exceptionally pure and well suited for agricultural purposes and the lime kilns situated beside the new line would ensure a widespread and continuing market for their product.

The blackshale seam outcrops at the southern end of Clay Cross tunnel and can be seen to this day in the approach cutting. Unlike some other seams its small-coal slack is useful and was recovered from the mines rather than being discarded and left. Stephenson saw the seam as a source of easily obtained coking fuel to supply the coke-burning engines of the Midland Railway and also as a cheap means of firing his lime kilns. Much later, after the ironworks had been established, the limestone which was used as the fluxing agent in the blast-furnaces was brought to the works from nearby Ashover quarry.

A small works was built at the north end of the tunnel and a bank of beehive-type coke-ovens built to supply the coke. All that was now required to complete the business was to sink a colliery – George Stephenson and Company had begun its long association with the town which now became Clay Cross. (The works begun by Stephenson have had different names over the years. In this story I have consistently used the name Clay Cross Company which was the name longest in use, and was in use when the events to be related occurred.)

In the year 1837, while the tunnel boring was still being pressed forward, two shafts 10 feet in diameter began sinking to the blackshale seam and the first coal from them was brought to bank the following year. This pit (only a portion of the waste heap remains today) was the Clay Cross No. 1, a pit that was later to play a large role in the tragedies at Clay Cross.

Deep Soft Seam

Deep Hard Seam

1st Piper Seam

2nd Piper Seam (Hospital, or Lower Piper) Old Man's Rake, Whetstone and Morley Park Dogtooth Rake

Tupton or Low Main

Butterley or Dogtooth Rake and Stripe Rake

Threequarter Seam

Yard Seam

Blackshale (Silkstone or Clod) Seam

Ashgate Seam
        Greenclose Rake, Holly Close Rake
Mickley Seam
        Black or Kellands Rake
Morley Muck Seam
        Yew Tree Rake
Kilburn Seam (Buckland Hollow Coal)
        Civilly, Dale Moor or Hagg Rake
Norton Seam

Alton Seam

1st Smalley Seam

Holbrook Seam

Belper Lawn Seam

Section not to scale

Ironstone shown:

Sequence of some of the coal seams and ironstone rakes of the middle and lower coal measures in Derbyshire.

Source: Terry Judge, "Some notes on the Alderwasley and Morley Park Ironworks and Mines", Derbyshire Miscellany 1993-94.

Chapter 5

COALMINING IN THE
DAYS OF GEORGE STEPHENSON

George Stephenson grew up in Northumberland around collieries. The pits around Killingworth where his father was an engine-man and where his own early reputation was first established, were old before he was born, he knew mines and was on intimate terms with the best of the northern mining engineers of his day.

John Buddle and Nicholas Wood were the pre-eminent mining engineers in those days, both had the view of vast coal empires in the north of England, at that time the leading area in all coal mining matters and up-to-date technology. Many of Stephenson's innovations and working plans were the result of long hours in the company of these and other practical miners, and it was many of Buddle's ideas that he incorporated in the layout of the Clay Cross pits.

The Northern System of working coal differed greatly from that practised elsewhere in the country, mainly in the actual recovery method, which can briefly be described under the following headings.

The Northern System or Pillar and Stall
Under this system a mine was divided into various districts, termed rooms and each room was then worked by small workings or headings, linked by cross-gates to carry the air flow forward, until the whole area resembled a chess-board in plan. When the room was fully developed the miner then went back to the furthest boundary and began to extract the pillars of coal left behind by the first working stalls. This pillar extraction is known as second working.

The Midlands System or Longwall Stall

The principle of longwall working, as its name implies, is the total extraction of all the available coal in one single operation, or first working, maintaining the roads by means of stone walls (packs), or by wooden props. In theory all the available coal can be extracted in a single operation without the need to ventilate great areas by tortuous courses of the air current (without which they would quickly become vast gasometers) and then have to return to extract, or partially extract, the pillars – which was always a dangerous undertaking.

Both systems have advantages and disadvantages and in the 19th century they excited much learned discussion and debate. The Northern System was certainly much more wasteful of reserves of coal and at first glance the history of explosions in the northern mines would tend to suggest that the system was much more dangerous to carry out, although there were other factors in that particular argument which have no bearing on this story. The pillar and stall method was not liked in the Midlands and from the archaeological evidence from opencast sites, it appears to have only been used near the outcrop of seams where they tend to be steeply inclined.

Before the advent of the beam pumping engine, deep mining was restricted by the problem of mine drainage. Virtually the only means of gaining access to deeper levels depended upon the driving, where possible, of long underground tunnels (soughs) which drained to some convenient point in a valley. Coal could be worked to the rise, or outcrop, of the seam and any water made in the workings flowed to the sough and then out of the mine.

The steam engine changed all that. The sough could now be taken under deep cover and instead of having to drain into a valley, could be pumped from its lowest point. The terminology changed at this point and soughs became known as water gates. They were the lowest possible working level of a mine. When the mine became worked out and the pumps were withdrawn the abandoned workings quickly flooded. As the next working was then set to the dip, or lower level of this abandoned pit, the flooded workings became a potential danger as the new coal-face advanced towards it. The theory that the keeping of accurate mine plans would guard against this eventuality, was exposed many times over the ensuing years as a myth, or at best, wishful thinking.

It sometimes happened that when an old worked-out pit

Plan and section of a stall in the Blackshale Seam which has left and right hand 'banks' laid with tub-rails.

was abandoned, one or more of its shafts could be connected with the new, deeper pit. These shafts, of little economic importance, were always very much desired by the workmen as they provided another means of escape should anything happen to the main shafts to cut the men off from the surface. They were termed basset pits and they are important to this story, we shall hear much of them.

The Clay Cross pits were laid out using the very best technology available at that time. During the inquests which followed the sad events related here, many details of the layout were made known and help to recreate the story.

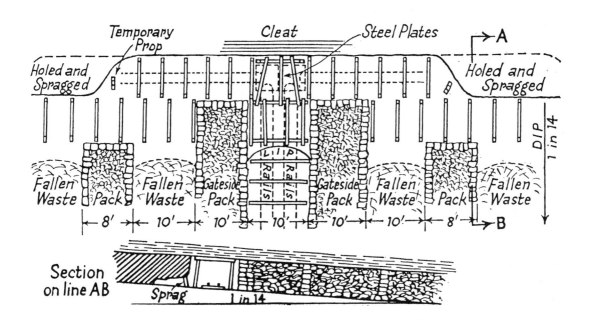

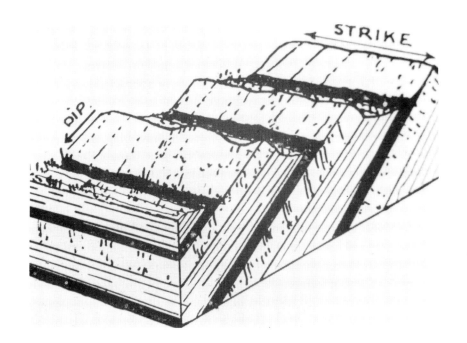

A section of inclined coal measures, showing 'dip' and 'strike'. Author's Collection.

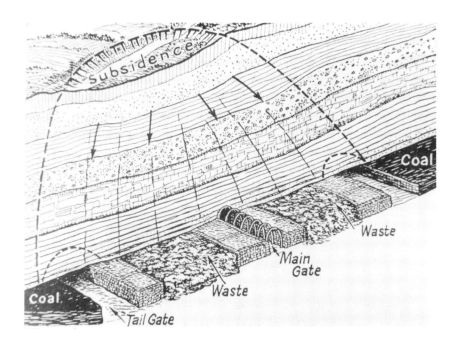

Schematic view of a coal face with a 'main gate' and 2 'tail gates', showing roof controlled by stone 'packs', and large 'wastes'. Also subsidence effect upon the surface. Author's Collection.

Chapter 6

THE CLAY CROSS PITS

Clay Cross No. 1 pit may well have been a stop-gap under-taking, sunk to supply an urgent need for coal in time for the opening of the Midland Railway. Certainly its life was not long even by 19th century standards; newer and better pits were still to come, and at the time when its shafts first began to draw coal Derbyshire mining was entering its 'Golden Age'. It was a time of investment, trade was improving, the railway was deliberately planned as, principally, a mineral line and ensured wide markets for the coal produced.

Instead of sinking his shafts strung-out over the line of a sough (Morley Park Old Level was over 2½ miles long, with five shafts and the outfall of the sough!), Stephenson sank two shafts 10 feet in diameter only 8 yards apart. The drawing shaft, or downcast, conveyed fresh air into the mine and was the main shaft for coal-winning. The upcast shaft was in effect nothing more than a huge chimney. A large furnace burned day and night at the bottom of the pit and drew fresh air down the downcast and by a system of doors and stoppings around the workings, ventilating the whole mine. near to the bottom of the shaft, a little fresh air was allowed to bleed off directly from the downcast, through a specially driven slit, or heading, to ventilate the furnace rather than passing mine air full of dangerous fumes and vapours over the flames. The smoke and fumes from the furnace connected with the upcast a few yards above the pit bottom, entrained the mine air which was prevented from entering the furnace but passed through the upcast pit bottom and was then passed up the shaft into the atmosphere. Upcast shafts were hot, smoky places but could not be entirely avoided by the men as they travelled between the surface and their workplaces.

The following is part of an account, written in 1856, of a descent into the deepest upcast shaft in Britain at that time, the famous Monkwearmouth Colliery near Sunderland, 1680 feet in depth (280 fathoms).

"In a couple of minutes, perhaps – the orifice of the shaft has apparently turned itself into a day-star, which shines far above you in the firmament, and which you may gaze at, like an astronomer... I have omitted one peculiar misery of this very shaft, because I did not want to smother you with smoke so soon; but, the fact is, this shaft is nothing but a wonderful chimney of eighteen hundred feet in depth! It is an upcast shaft, and the ventilating furnace is at the bottom. All the return air, charged with various impurities and all the furnace smoke (and an immense fire is kept roaring in that furnace), ascend through this shaft which you have been descending. No wonder a companion of mine, in descending, dropped down to the bottom of the tub. He says he felt half choked, another minute he declares, would have made his wife a widow! Well it is no small trifle to go down an upcast of this enormous depth, and to be every moment getting nearer and nearer to the roaring furnace, a glimpse of whose glowing brightness you get as you go by. Going up in a balloon is nothing to going down this shaft; for in a balloon you rise into purer air – in the coal shaft you sink continually into fouler gloom and more fiery darkness".

The shafts at Clay Cross were sunk at the lowest level of the future take (area to be fully worked) of the mine and the ventilation system and working plan was considered to be modern and was highly approved of.

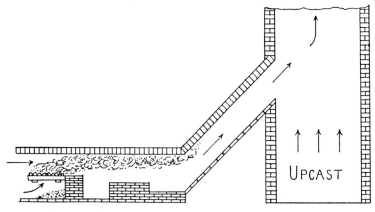

The underground furnace for ventilating mines in former days. The heated and lighter air ascended the upcast shaft and entrained the warm mine air after it. The fresh air descended another shaft connected by mine workings to the upcast shown.

Chapter 7

THE NUMBER 1 PIT

Twenty years ago when I first began to research this story, living at number 10, Pine Close, Danesmoor, was the late Mr Ernest Walker, who for 20 years was an overman at Parkhouse Colliery. Among his papers Mr Walker had a document listing prices and duties to be carried out by contractors working in George Stephenson and Company pits. It is addressed to a man named Martin and is well over 140 years old. It was common practice in the 19th century to lease out the underground working of the pits to contractors who had to sign such documents listing the requirements of the Company in respect to the working of the coal, and the underground conduct of the mine. When the system was eventually abandoned due to better legislation, many of these contractors became corporals, deputies, or overmen. Most were good, practical pitmen with wide mining knowledge. One such contractor was this Martin. Martin appears to have been a personal favourite of Stephenson, he may of course have been one of his famed Northumbrians, because shortly after signing the contract Martin was put on the company payroll and appointed underviewer, a staff position. He appears to have held this position for about four years and it is part of those years which concern our story.

In 19th century practice, as described in Chapter 6, once the pit bottom arrangements and the water-level (gate) had been driven at right angles to the dip of the seam, headings were driven, following the natural slope of the strata, upwards towards the outcrop. This enabled any water which entered the working faces to flow away towards the downcast pit to be pumped to the surface. Clay Cross was notoriously heavily watered and the mine had been carefully laid out with this fact in mind.

From the scant evidence which is now available it would appear that Martin was not very competent, although the reader is left to judge whether or not Martin was later made a scapegoat! He was replaced by a younger man, John Parker, around 1841. Parker, in later years, was unable to remember the exact date (which is a little surprising in view of his later, very detailed evidence), but some time between 1837 and 1841, while he was overman under Martin, there occurred an accident at the colliery which was to have serious repercussions 20 years later.

The coal at No. 1 pit was easily won. Large stalls (long-wall working faces), were opened out at right angles to the water gate, employing up to eight men in each stall. High tonnages were achieved and after some initial difficulty in getting a fickle public to accept the new coal, the pit began to prosper.

John Parker remembered going over the plan of the mine in the pit office one morning and while doing so became disturbed by something he saw. He decided to go down the pit and investigate. He entered the cage and was soon in the pit bottom, from where he made his way to a district of the pit known as the deep level (the water gate). It was not part of his duties to be in that part of the mine and he alleged later that it was only curiosity which led him there at all.

All the water made in the pit flowed along the Deep Level toward the shafts; but in the summer months, when the flow sometimes dried up altogether, it was possible to work a little of the coal which lay to the dip of the level. This was now being done and five little stalls, each employing two men, were dipping down eastward away from the drainage level. Parker had evidently seen something on the plan which disturbed him; the stalls were not found to be recorded at a later date and we shall never know exactly what drew him there. The practice was highly dangerous but nevertheless was often carried out to get easy coal, often with the same tragic results.

Parker said later that on the day when curiosity drew him to the workings, none of the stalls were at work, but one man was driving a small heading which was even further down the dip slope, away from the water gate and in advance of the line of five stalls. It would appear that this heading, being driven in a very dry period when little or no water was entering the mine, was intended to be a sump. It could never be reached by the mine pump and was therefore illegal! Parker would have been well aware of this fact. The five small headings appear to have been intended as a water-lodgement area, as a temporary measure. I can find no evidence on the existing plan for No. 1 pit of a steam-powered pump sited in the pit bottom, therefore it must be assumed that the pumps were operated from a surface engine with its suction sited in the pit-bottom sump. Any water which later filled this new lodgement could never be pumped and would forever remain a hazard, it is small wonder that the plan could never be produced, and yet one must have existed for Parker to have said what he did?

Parker stated that when he entered the man's stall, the work was being carried out in a very sloppy manner and the workman seemed surprised that he (Parker) was in the district at all. Parker reproved him sharply, telling him that the coal that he was cutting needed sprags (short wooden temporary supports) and to get them set without delay, "Or you will find yourself buried"! Parker then left the lone workman and went to his own district; two hours later he heard that the man had disregarded his advice and that the coal had broken down and killed him.

To the best of Parker's knowledge the place where the man was killed was never worked again *and was never entered on the plan of the mine*. Martin had been in charge of the mine — what his objective had been in approving the heading, Parker could not say. The matter was to rest there, forgotten by Parker and unknown to anyone else, for 20 years, when the man who worked alone would be violently resurrected and his lonely and untimely death brought to public attention.

It is perhaps helpful to summarise certain points here before moving on. According to Parker's own sworn evidence, something that he saw on the plan drew him to check the work below the Deep Level, yet it was later shown that nothing irregular had been entered on the plan! It seems surprising that this point was not further pursued. One final point later came out, Martin was held in high regard by Mr Stephenson and reported directly to him. By the time that these facts came out, the lone workman, Stephenson, and Martin also, were all long dead and beyond the reach of a Coroner's questions!

In 1842 Mr J.M. Fellowes, H.M. sub-commissioner for Derbyshire, took evidence for the Royal Commission on Employment of Children (Mines). After dealing with various arrangements made by the company for the benefit of its workforce, his report makes the following observations. "I found the ventilation plan adopted by George Stephenson and Company at Clay Cross fully answered that gentleman's requirements. It was by sinking two shafts within a few yards of each other and placing a furnace at the bottom of one, this creating a current of air through the whole works in a superior manner to any that I have seen before". Mr Fellowes had received some rough treatment during his perambulations on the coalfield and had been deeply shocked by many of his experiences – this was high praise indeed.

Mr Fellowes talked with the workforce (when they would talk to him!) wherever he went. Although many were suspicious of his motives, believing that he was seeking to take bread from their mouths by removing small children from mines, he found the men at Clay Cross happy with their employer; they all agreed that their situations had very much improved, far better than at any pit they had previously worked in. These men had come from many parts, mostly from villages with centuries-old traditions of mining, some from coalfields which are now long forgotten, they knew from bitter experience what they were praising.

Courtesy of Cliff Williams.

No. 113.]   **OFF UP.**   [*See No. 122.*
Colliers—getters of the "C.X.C. Gold Medal" Coal—being hauled from bottom of shaft to surface 300 yards above.

Chapter 8

THE NUMBER 2 PIT

In the year 1846 the Clay Cross Company began the production of iron on the site of the present works. Two blast furnaces were erected and ironstone pits sunk in the locality. Coal was now being sent by rail as far as London and as the public acceptance of the new coal grew (the blackshale has some strange properties, the railway historian tells some amusing tales of the company agents' attempts to promote the coal when local markets had been used to such seams as the Kilburn, Denby Hard, and Deep Soft, whose properties were well liked and understood), it was found that the pit could not satisfy all the demand. A decision was taken to sink further pits, resulting in the founding of pits Nos. 2 and 3 in the works yard.

The sinking of No. 2 took four years and during this time the company changed the face of Clay Cross. The expected large labour force, all to be imported, needed housing, education and hospital arrangements. Much of this work fell upon Charles Binns the company secretary.

In the year 1850, at the time of the Great Exhibition at the Crystal Palace, and two years after the death of George Stephenson, No. 2 and a further new pit No. 4, brought their first coal to bank. No. 4 pit was situated out of the works yard and some distance to the north, close to North Wingfield and Tupton from whence most of its workforce was drawn.

John Parker, the young overman of No. 1 pit had done well for himself and was now head underviewer. The term is difficult to explain today; at first sight it would appear to mean the same as a modern-day undermanager, but in the mid-19th century his powers were wider, more like a present day group manager. Employed directly by the company, usually with a stated number of perquisites, he took his orders from the company engineer, who in turn consulted and was advised by, the consulting engineer, or viewer. Coalmining legislation was still in its infancy in 1850 and it was to be some years yet before the appointment of properly certificated managers who had sat a formal examination and received a recognised certificate of competence.

No. 2 pit was sunk to the east and to the dip (lower in the same seam) of the old No. 1 pit which ceased production in 1849-50. No. 1, its workings now abandoned, began slowly to fill with water. Blackdamp, the dreaded gas (mainly carbon-dioxide) that always forms in old workings, began to add its own insidious presence as soon as the ventilation was withdrawn.

Before the advent of modern earth-moving equipment, it was difficult (if it was even considered) to eradicate all signs of where a colliery had once been. The newer workforce would have eyed the abandoned surface works and pondered upon their meaning in relation to their own situation. (The miner has always had a pretty good idea of where he was underground in relation to the surface.) Then, as now, they would have talked to the older workforce; in the pubs and at 'snap breaks', talk would touch upon the danger lurking in the old workings. It was well known to the men in No. 2 pit that they were working beneath pent-up water, they called it 'the top shale water' (No. 1 pit was the Top Pit) and they were working towards it!

Some time in 1859 Charles Binns wrote to the District Inspector of Mines, Mr Hedley. Binns informed the inspector that he intended to work the coal close to the old No. 1 workings. The inspector visited Clay Cross and met Mr Binns and John Parker. The trio then went carefully over the plans of both collieries and Mr Hedley suggested that a fresh survey should be done and that a solid barrier of coal, at least 15 yards thick, should be left between the two pits to keep the water out of No. 2 pit. Some weeks later Charles Binns personally carried out the re-survey and instructed the company's consulting engineer, Robert Stephenson, to conduct his own independent survey. These surveys *assumed* the complete accuracy of the plans of the old No. 1 workings, since it was impossible now to gain access into that pit to check the results. At best, the new survey was only half-a-job given those circumstances, and as had happened many times before and since, it was to lead to tragedy.

The question of leaving barriers between pits was a long-standing bone of contention, not just between the men and the mine owner, but often between the coal owner and the mineral lessee also. If a barrier 20 yards wide, two yards high, and say, half a mile long, were to be left this represented a considerable loss of coal which could never be recovered, therefore both coal owner and mine manager were often reluctant to agree over their proportions. The men on the other hand understandably wanted assurances that if barriers were left, they were wide enough and completely accurate. The solution, as the men saw it, was to penetrate the old workings as quickly as possible so that pits lying to the 'rise' could not accumulate water and the old shafts could be used as basset shafts in emergency. With newer pumping arrangements this was sometimes possible, but very often barriers had to be left, and because of the notorious inaccuracy of the plans, they were always a potential danger.

The new surveys were brought together with the old plans and all three checked remarkably well. Binns decided to forego a little coal in the interests of safety, and also to dispense with the necessity of boring from underground to find the old workings, by more than doubling Mr. Hedley's recommended barrier to 40 yards in thickness. It all looked

Mr. Hedley's plan of the stalls at the top of 'Dan's Incline' and the position of Dawes' stall where the breach occurred. Dan's Incline is shown as: "self-acting incline", lower centre of photograph. Author's Collection.

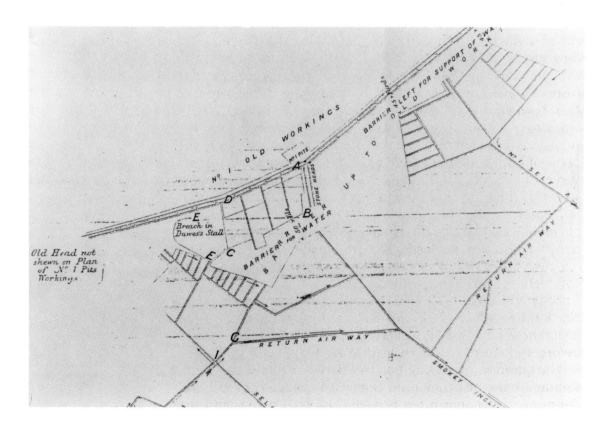

35

fine – well-surveyed, properly entered on the plans, the inspectors suggestions more than complied with, what could possibly go wrong? They were soon to find out! What none of them knew, and John Parker had long ago forgotten about, were those five little stalls that Martin had worked all those years ago, along with the mysterious heading where the lone collier had died, that had penetrated far beyond the point that they now assumed was safe. It was nearly time to resurrect the long-dead collier.

Note the meagre light cast by the safety lamp. Courtesy of Cliff Williams.

No. 107.] DOWN A COAL MINE.
Blacksmith performing his daily duties in the stables in one of the Pits producing the renowned "C.X.C. Gold Medal" Coal.

Chapter 9

THE 1861 INUNDATION

11th June

Rising up towards the old No. 1 workings from near No. 2 pit bottom was a long tunnel known as Dan's Incline. It lay about 400 yards across the dip from the shafts. At the top of this incline some stalls were working towards the proposed barrier.

In one of these stalls, No. 177 Blackshale, worked Nathaniel Dawes and his loader, Thomas Boden. The stall was reckoned to be around 14 yards short of the intended barrier. When it reached that point the stall would close and Dawes would head-out another stall in a different area of the pit.

That morning the pair had gone down the pit at 5.30 in company with 155 other men and boys, and trudged along the main level towards Dan's Incline carrying lighted candles. When they reached 177 stall it stood 'straight up' or in other words all the coal had been loaded out and Dawes had to undercut the face, called 'holing out', in order to break down another 'web' and advance the face. Boden lit his own candle and stuck it by means of a special nail to a convenient prop, out of the swing of his pick, and began to form a vertical cut from floor to roof which would eventually free the mass of coal that his mate was now undercutting. Harsh breathing, grunts, and the rhythmic sound of picks striking coal were the only sounds that could be heard. Around 9.30a.m. a boy, John Bradbury, arrived with his pony and four empty tubs. They were about 15 yards in from the top of the incline and heard him spin the tubs and push them into the stall road.

Nathaniel (Natty) Dawes was a member of the elite of any pit, an experienced hewer, he was senior man in the stall. Longwall working, as already explained meant that the stalls, or working places, advanced towards a line drawn on the plan, taking the whole of the available coal, and the entire face-line ended when the workings reached that planned point. Because underground conditions varied from stall to stall, or some hewers were quicker workmen than others, there are a variety of reasons, some stalls stopped before others and the face-line was never as straight as may be supposed.

Coal is not an amorphous substance, it has grain and natural partings which can be utilised by the miner and which aid him in getting the coal. Modern machine-mining takes advantage of this grain and works the coal along its natural face, which facilitates easy breaking down of the mass, resulting in small coal which the power-station market demands, and makes for easier blending of seams at the surface. In the days of hand-worked stalls entirely the opposite was required and the stalls were usually set out on 'end or half-end', which is like working a piece of wood against its natural grain; this resulted in large round coal, but was obviously harder to hew.

A stallman began the coalgetting process by first lying on his side and cutting a horizontal slot under the face. He supported the undercut coal with short temporary supports called sprags until the entire length was undermined and supported by the sprags. His mate meanwhile cut a vertical slot from floor to roof called the 'buttock', this gave the mass of coal another free end; properly done under ideal conditions, the coal would then fall in huge lumps when the sprags were withdrawn. The process was dangerous, carried out in very poor lighting conditions and it was not easy to get out of the way, especially from a supine position, if the mass began to move without warning.

At 10.45a.m. the two paused for a short 'snap' and lit tobacco pipes. They just had them drawing well when footsteps were heard in the stall-gate and the leather-capped head of the overman, followed by that of his corporal, appeared under the lip. George Parker, nephew of the head underviewer, chided the men gently and coaxed them back to work. As Boden began to cut more sprags the senior officials took a good look round and, seemingly finding everything in good order, passed on to visit the adjacent stalls. The corporal, Alfred Smith, had a difficult job. Although mainly responsible for the young lads on the haulage and transport, corporals in his day acted very much as modern day deputies, and Smith was in fact responsible, under Parker, for all the stalls at the top of Dan's Incline.

No. 102.] **300 YARDS BELOW GROUND.** [See No. 111.
Two typical Colliers winning their bread getting the celebrated "C.X.C. Gold Medal" Coal.

Courtesy of Cliff Williams.

Around 2.00p.m. Dawes completed holing and the pair began to draw the sprags and allow the coal to break down. Boden was almost opposite to the stall-gate when he noticed that water was beginning to stream out of the face near the foot of the seam. They took little notice at first and began to fill the four tubs, but one hour later, as they pushed a tub out into the gate, Dawes noticed that the flow of water had quickened; a regular stream had now formed and was flowing out of the stall and along the gently dipping gate towards the top of the incline.

John Bradbury came up the gate with his pony at 3.30p.m. and noticed a strong flow coming out of the face, he went under the lip for a closer look and then called out to the stallman, "Hey Natty, hasta seen all this water?" Dawes and Boden came down for another look, the lad hitched his full tubs to the pony and departed. The two colliers stared at the water, now increasing in strength as the flow quickened ever more, it was while they were trying to decide what to do about it that Boden mentioned the old workings.

Dawes became thoroughly frightened now and told his mate to get dressed. They gathered their tools together, dressed quickly and left the stall at 4.00p.m. When they reached the incline, the corporal's young son, Timothy Smith, was hitching full coal-tubs onto the rope prior to sending them down to the main haulage level which ran at right angles to the dip of the strata into the upcast pit bottom. (In order to avoid confusion, this description was left out of the general account of the layout of the pit until this point. A level generally means what the word implies – a long, straight road on a more or less level plane. Inclines dip, or climb away from the levels following the natural slope of the strata. Most intake inclines were used to convey coal down to the main haulage roads whilst return inclines were for the passage of air and sometimes supplies. The full tubs were lowered by means of a simple device called a jig, a large wheel, fitted with a brake, around which passed a rope. When in operation, a set number of full tubs were fixed to the rope at the top of the incline and a set number of empty ones were fastened to the other end at the bottom, these were known as tub sets. When ready, the gravity of the full set descending drew the empties up the incline, a boy controlled the speed and motion by operating a simple brake mechanism, the whole arrangement was called a self acting incline. Ponies generally hauled the coal tubs from the stalls to the top of the inclines and continuous haulage systems, or ponies in smaller mines, hauled them along the levels to the pit bottom.)

Dawes asked the lad where his father was working and was told "In the stallgate next but one to yours, he is laying some rails". If Dawes was as worried as his later testimony implied, it was not great distance for him to have returned and confronted Alfred Smith with his fears, but he did not do so, instead, he told Timothy "Be sure and tell your father about the water when you see him". The boy assured him that he would do so and Dawes and Boden hurried towards the pit bottom to be drawn to safety at the surface.

Sam Bamford worked the next stall inbye (about 15 yards further in) to Dawes. Bamford and his mate, Henry Bostock had also finished work for the day and were leaving. When they came to the end of Dawes' stall-gate they met the young pony driver Bradbury. The boy told them about the water in the stall, and as he passed on, he called out to them "Natty thinks that it is the Top Shale Water!" The two men stared at each other, then decided to go and look for themselves. When they reached the face they saw a quick stream of water, as thick as a man's arm, issuing from an area of coal close to the gate end and about six feet wide. Bamford decided to return to his own stall and fetch out his picks, it never occurred to him to warn anyone of the impending danger, which was now less than an hour away! They too entrusted a hurried warning to young Smith and passed on into safety.

A few more men passed the boy who was naturally getting worried by this time. The reader, forewarned, wants to shake him, send him hurrying to his father – anything to make him aware of his imminent danger, "Get up Timothy, get out while there is still a chance!" The boy stays at his post. About ten minutes afterwards the relieved boy saw his father approaching and blurted out the message that Dawes had given him adding that "Natty thinks it is the Top Shale Water!" Alfred Smith smiled at his son's anxious face; he was an experienced miner with some knowledge of the pit plans, and he knew that at least 50 yards of solid coal lay before Dawes' stall. Still, it would do no harm to have a look. "We will just have-a-minute Tim and then we will go and have a look at it." The elder Smith sat down beside his son and took out his pipe. He had just taken a contented pull when a dull rumble was heard coming from somewhere near the top of the incline. "That will be the putter (Bradbury) with another set for thee lad". But it was no putter. Just as Alfred Smith sat down to light his pipe, the pent-up waters in the old pit found their release through two feet of rotten coal in the gate end of No. 177 stall.

Plan produced by Inspector Hedley showing detail of the breach in Dawes Stall 1861. Authors Collection.

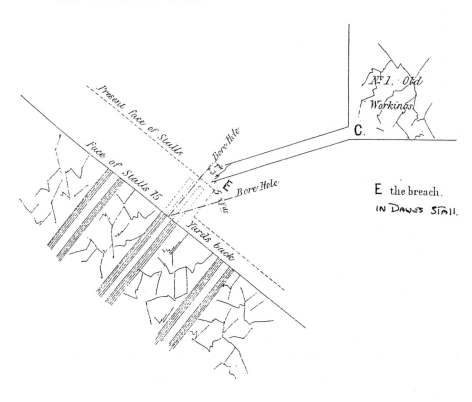

11th June, 5.00p.m. to 7.00p.m.
One word sums up the events of the next two tense hours.
Panic!

The sad fact is that it was, with a couple of noteworthy
exceptions, the wrong people who panicked. When Alfred
Smith and his son heard the water burst out of Dawes' stall
and come roaring down the incline towards them, they too
must have experienced that heart-lurching breath-snatching
moment that every underground worker knows only too
well at some time or another, that unvoiced half-expected,
dreaded moment when the unknown leaps out of the darkness and only luck, lightning reactions or the will of the
Almighty determine the final outcome.

Smith kept his head. He sent his lad towards the pit bottom and turned himself to face the flood. He was the corporal; it was his duty to get his men to safety. Running down
into the dip-workings where he had three men and three
young boys at work, Smith got them all together and led
them to Dan's Incline. The water was by now rushing down,
and they had great difficulty in finding and keeping their feet.
At last they had to stop and force their way through some
doors into the return airway. This led to a long incline
known as the Smoky Incline which in turn led directly to the
upcast shaft (hence, smoky).

The water was already deep in the return airway and the
young boys with him were afraid and begged him to turn
back. At this point a lump of stone fell from the roof and put
out his candle leaving them in the dark. There was nothing
for it but to return through the doors where, back in Dan's
Incline, Smith got out his matches and managed to relight his
candle (it was far too dangerous to strike a naked flame in
the foul air of the return airway). After hunting around he
found a small tin in which he placed his candle, then, keeping
the boys close to him, he got back through the water, now
rapidly filling the return, down the Smoky Incline to the pit
bottom, where he found that there was already half-a-yard
of water, and sent the young boys up the shaft.

Over 60 years after these events my grandfather was still
working with the aid of candles in the old Lower Hartshay
Colliery near Ripley. The old safety lamps shed very little
light and in consequence were detested by the men. The
tallow-dips, manufactured from animal fat gave a better
illumination, but were extremely dangerous in use (there will
be more on this point later, see page 103). Smoking was
allowed in the pits but not of course in the return airways.

Bad lighting probably led to more deaths among hewers than any other single cause.

Thomas Boden was one of three men warned and sent out by Smith, he started on his way outbye. Encountering four boys he made them join him. The two smallest were Alfred Smith's youngest son, aged 13, and Henry Oldfield, also 13. Boden stripped himself to the waist when he reached the water, and, catching each of the boys under his arms he plunged into the torrent. Boden and his charges were knocked off their feet and swilled to the bottom of the incline. Here he found two more boys, one of whom was working his first shift in the pit, and although he still had the two youngest in his arms, he took charge of the pair, hanging tightly to his belt.

Not far from the pit bottom they were all swilled against some air-doors, the mud and water now being about four feet deep. Boden clung to his half-drowned, frightened charges and fought his way to the bottom of the shaft; they reached the surface at 5.15p.m.

When Timothy Smith ran down Dan's incline and reached the main haulage level, he had the guts to turn inbye (away from the shafts) to warn the haulage corporal James Booth; this was at around 4.35p.m. Booth sent a few of the boys working with him towards the pit bottom with Timothy, but did nothing to warn the corporal working further inbye, although it was later alleged that he had ample time to have done so. Booth was the first of the officials to panic. He rushed off to the pit bottom and, unbelievably, even sent the onsetter (person in charge of the cages), who should have been the last person to leave his post, out of the pit.

The next corporal inbye of Booth was Samuel Wood, aged 19. He heard the water breaking in at 4.50p.m., when a putter boy, Thomas Howitt, ran and told him that the black-shale water had broken into the pit. Wood had five boys under him, one of whom as Joseph Ashmore. Wood later said that he told Ashmore to get out of the pit as quickly as possible, but why he took the other four boys and left Ashmore, he never explained and we shall never know. He said that he never saw the lad again. He was to hear much of him later! Wood was the second official to panic and fail in his duty.

Perhaps the most pathetic case of panic was that of a corporal in charge of a district known as the Stone Heads. A stone heading is a drift or underground roadway, either up or down, connecting one seam with another. In this case it was being driven upwards from the blackshale seam to the overlying Tupton-Threequarters seam. A heading has only one entrance and exit, there is no other means of communication with other districts. Six hundred yards from the shafts, the stone heads were isolated from the rest of the mine, when completed they would have formed the main inclines into the newly developed seam.

Benjamin Wright was the corporal in charge of the district. That day he had three development workers actually at work in the heading, and one putter boy with his pony to take away the tunnelling debris. Wright heard about the accident shortly after he had fired some shots, probably from the putter, at around 5.00p.m. He rushed from his district and did his best to render aid to the other corporals. By the time he reached the surface the water was filling the pit bottom, and only then did the awful realisation hit him; he had forgotten his own men! Only four persons in his charge, all of whom had ample time to have escaped, but were now hopelessly trapped in the headings, sealed in by the rising water and being poisoned by the fumes from the shotfiring which were now unventilated.

When Natty Dawes got out of the pit his mind was troubled with thoughts of the water. No doubt the sight of the old No. 1 pit which was on his way home, added to his misgivings. For whatever reason, he decided to report to George Parker and give a first-hand account to the overman. He called at Parker's house but was told that he was out visiting a sick man in Long Row and would not be back for some time. A man named Grainger was working in his garden next door to Parker's house and promised to give him a message when he returned. Satisfied, Dawes started once again for home, he had still not reached it when the pit blower began to wail out its unwelcome warning that all was not well in the pit.

George Parker's adventures in the flooded pit began after Grainger, who would have realised from the wailing blower that Dawes' misgivings were now all too true, had run to the sick man's house to appraise him of the fact. The pit was flooding fast when he arrived. Parker, accompanied by the indomitable Alfred Smith, went to the upcast shaft and they were quickly lowered to the pit bottom. They found two men trying to open the air doors in the slit (a narrow passage) which linked the two shafts. The men thought that some others were trapped behind the doors. They began to knock out the brickwork but at that moment the furnace began to lose its air supply and smoke and fumes started to cast back down the shaft. The half-choked men returned to the surface, but after recovering they decided to try once more. A few moments work with the hammers and a small hole was opened, through which poured torrents of water. Smith reached through the opening and dragged out the half-drowned body of a small boy, George Bunce. They carried the boy between them, and just had time to ring off the cage before the pit bottom flooded completely.

In the downcast pit bottom it was also time to go. Three men stood upon the chair (another term for the cage) which had been raised up about three feet. One of the men was the courageous Boden, who had already given much of himself in his efforts to save others. They waited until the water began to wash onto the very floor of the chair and then sadly rang for the engine to lift them out. At that very moment Boden saw a tiny hand raised above the swirling stream, and snatched another, final soul, as the engine lifted them for the last time. A moment later and the water began remorselessly, to climb the shaft. Air bubbles burst beneath them, flotsam surged to the surface, forming a dirty, swirling pool. The pit was drowned out. The half-voiced fears which the men had carried for over 20 years had at last been brought to tragic realisation, the Top Shale Water, the bogey man of their worst nightmares, was loose in the No. 2 pit.

Descending the shaft the old way. Note the winding chain, these replaced 'flat' ropes, and were themselves replaced by steel cables.

Chapter 10

THE RESCUE ATTEMPT

The normal reaction of a mining community, when disaster strikes a pit, is to rush to the pit-head for news. Today, news at such disasters is carefully handled, sanitised with cautious press releases, carefully worded television and radio bulletins, the curious kept back from the scene of activity, the press told only as much as is deemed necessary. A tried and tested system of operations swings into action, the pit's own rescue team, the area rescue team, medical assistance, police, and other vital quick-reaction organisations are called upon and within minutes are responding to that call. It was all so different in 1861.

When the hooter blared out its shocking warning at 5.55p.m. that afternoon, a large and anxious crowd gathered around the pit mouth. Within minutes of the disaster being made known the news was spread far and wide. The local press sent reporters along and they were soon active among the crowd, ignored by the few harassed officials present at the scene, they sought their 'news' in sensationalism and pathos.

The establishment of a quick-response, central rescue station was still 50 years into the future at that time. Volunteers, called for and quickly offered from among the crowd, made up make-shift rescue parties, men willing to face untold horrors and unknown dangers, untrained except for their natural abilities, with no special equipment, they shot their hands in the air every time a call was made. Mining history owes a great debt to these thousands of unsung heroes who, on every coalfield in Great Britain, gave of their guts, and all-too-often their lives, to bring succour to their mates. It will seem unbelievable today to learn that when the midland coal owners finally, belatedly got around to funding and establishing a central rescue station, the idea was vigorously opposed on the grounds *that it would never justify its expense!*

A *Derbyshire Times* reporter described the early scenes around the pit mouth. "Women and children were crying for news of husbands, fathers and loved ones, as each chair was landed, disgorging its pathetic half-drowned cargo upon the bank, the wild-eyed crowd dashed forward unto the very mouth of the void, desperately seeking their loved ones, pressing the few lucky survivors for any grain of information, unwilling, even when the water was filling the shafts, to accept the fact that nothing further could be done for their lost ones".

At that time the District Inspector of Mines was based at an office on London Road, Derby. John Parker telegraphed at once to alert the inspector, then turned his attention to marshalling what help he could muster from local sources. Telegrams set the wires buzzing alongside the railway as the aid of other mining engineers, drawn from the managements at local collieries was urgently canvassed, and quickly responded to. The company's own consulting engineer was fetched, anyone Parker could contact, who could offer positive help or advice; he was to spend some anxious, harassing days in the immediate future.

It was nearly high summer, the time of year when traditionally the coal trade slowed as the market demand fell. Pits worked less, some stalls were stopped altogether, awaiting the winter when, hopefully trade would increase again. The collier counted his dwindling coppers, tightened his belt, or sought consolation in the pub, chapel, or his garden, his 'betters', packed their bags, gathered their families and departed, seeking whatever delights the mid-Victorian age had to offer, far from the dirty, cholera-prone environment of the average pit village.

Charles Binns was just returning from his holiday that evening. At 8.20p.m. he was standing on the platform at Derby Station awaiting a local connection which would be stopping at Clay Cross. Glancing along the platform, he was no doubt surprised, but not unduly alarmed, to see the District Inspector Mr Hedley, a man he knew well, approaching him with an anxious look upon his face, moments later the company secretary also wore that same look of worry, all thoughts of his holiday suppressed, as Hedley broke the news and gave him what little information he had. The railway company put them aboard the first available fast train, and stopped it especially for them in the cutting beside the works. They made the journey in 25 minutes.

At 9.00p.m. that evening a small group gathered in Charles Binns' office. Present, besides himself and Mr Hedley, were William Howe the well-known and respected company Chief Engineer, Robert Stevenson the company Mining Engineer (no relation to George Stephenson) and Mr Campbell with his son George, who were consultant mining engineers, based in Matlock. The plans of Nos. 1, 2 and 4 pits lay before them on the table. Mr Howe had already had the cages removed from the flooded shafts and a large iron tub (iron barrel) was being endlessly raised and lowered as quickly as possible to try and lower the still filling shafts.

After much deliberation it was decided that the rescue operation would consist of: –
1. Fitting larger iron tubs at No. 2 upcast shaft.
2. Fitting a 30hp steam pump to No. 2 downcast shaft.
3. Gaining entry into the old No. 1 workings.
4. Driving a heading from No. 4 pit into the northside workings of No. 2 pit.

Mr Campbell and his son were put in charge of the No. 1 pit operation and the No. 4 pit heading was to be supervised by that pit's overman, John Brown.

While the meeting was still in progress, further bad news was brought in. A group of men standing by the pit mouth had heard a dull rumbling which emanated from the workings. It was surmised that some of the men now trapped below, in the higher parts of the mine, had fired some gas, now that the ventilation had been stopped, and this had caused an explosion! Whatever the real cause, nothing was ever mentioned on the matter, and no evidence of explosive gas was found when the workings were eventually re-entered. Mine shafts and wells greatly magnify sound. These rumblings were heard some five hours after the shafts were closed and I think it possible that what was heard were large air-bubbles, propelled by the pressure in the mine as the flood increased, venting in the shaft.

John Brown went back to No. 4 pit to organise the heading: this was begun the same night. This heading, 6 feet high and 6 feet wide, was to progress at an amazing 10 yards a day through a solid barrier of coal, using only picks and shovels. Brown, later said of the men: "They cut coal at an amazing rate; in fact at times we had difficulty shifting it away from them. Never before have I seen coal cut at such a rate!"

Work went on carefully in all the different operations. It was felt that the 23 men and boys thought to be trapped (they were not certain of the actual number) stood a good chance of survival. There were plenty of ponies in the pit, and men had been known to keep alive for 16 weeks in a northern pit, living on the flesh of ponies. It was said that the water now filling the pit was full of iron and could not be drunk, but there were ample barrels of fresh water in parts of the mine which would not be flooded.

14th June

Great excitement was caused on 14th June when the two Campbells succeeded in getting down No. 1 pit which they reported as being now quite dry. An exploring party went down and were gone for some hours; when they returned to the surface, hope began to rise for the trapped men. Mr Jeffcock, another well-known Derbyshire mining engineer, thought that it might be possible to enter the northside workings in No. 2 pit from there, as the old workings were now quite dry, and free from blackdamp and inflammable gas. "They only have to drive through thirty yards of coal, which, if they progress at the same rate as the men driving the heading in No. 4, they will be through, and into the No. 2 in three days."

Work was started, but the miners found that they could not support the rotten roof, and the next morning it came crashing down burying five of them. They were dug out in time, but the idea was given up, and now all hopes were resting on No. 4 heading, and the ceaselessly working pumps. New, larger tubs had been fitted and 19,000 gallons per hour were being brought to the surface.

On the Sunday following the accident, a rumour was started that the trapped men had been heard crying out to be saved. Such rumours were frequent at mining accidents, not malicious in intent, they mirrored the crowd's inevitable hopes and frustrations, the news-hungry reporters snapped up such snippets, which, when printed only served to raise false hopes among the wider, less informed readership.

The days dragged on. One day hopes would rise, only to be dashed as a tub broke or the pump stopped. The tub was fitted with a trip mechanism which was operated by the banksman's foot to empty its contents at the surface. One day the tub went a little higher than usual and the man narrowly missed being cast down the shaft as he over balanced!

29th June

At last they started to make some impression. On 29th June the water level in the shaft dropped by 15 feet, and the next

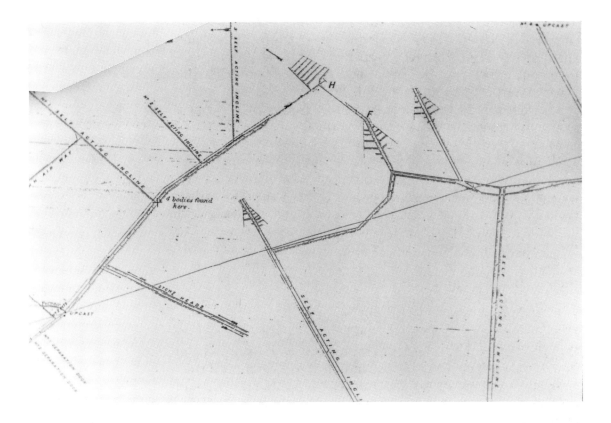

Plan of part of the workings of No.'s 2 and 4 pits in 1861. The line drawn H–F shows the position of the heading which John Brown and his men drove through the barrier separating the two pits. Author's Collection.

day it was well below the entrance to the furnace drift, some yards above the pit bottom. Mr Hedley assembled the engineers and they fastened a safety lamp to the bottom of the tub and lowered it halfway down the shaft. The lamp returned to the surface burning brightly. They lowered it again, this time to the mouth of the furnace drift; again the flame still burned when the tub returned. (This simple test was carried out to ensure that there was no blackdamp present before men were lowered.)

A party immediately got into the tub and were slowly lowered to the level of the mouth of the drift. The party advanced slowly down the dripping, brick-lined incline; the air was foul and suddenly a terrible sickly stench rose up in their nostrils. The ponies stabled nearby had all been drowned in their stalls and now the decaying bodies added their unwelcome stench to the odours of the pit. Chloride of lime was quickly sent down and liberally spread, but on trying to progress further into the workings the safety lamp suddenly went out. This was what they had most feared; it now looked as if the pit was full of blackdamp, which had been drawn in with the water from the old workings, they

51

returned to the surface without delay.

Another consultation resulted in a decision to complete the pumping out of the water and then try to get the ventilation going again. A steam pipe was installed during the next two days; the pipe was perforated near the bottom so that as the hot steam issued from the holes and rose back up the shaft it created a current of air, drawing with it the air from the mine. It appears that this was ineffectual, and meanwhile, all hopes rested with the heading being driven from No. 4 pit. Here John Brown and his men had performed wonders. The barrier of coal separating the two pits was 157 yards thick, and on 3rd July, around midnight, the tired, sweating men eventually broke through the last few feet.

Headings such as this one would today be excavated by machines. It was a similar type of heading to this, only wider, in which the tragedy at Bilsthorpe Colliery, Notting-hamshire, occurred in 1993. Assuming that Brown and his men, after suitable preparation, began work on the day following the accident, the drivage took exactly 21 days to complete. Using picks and shovels, presumably working only with safety lamps, in a cramped 6 feet wide passage where the coal was always difficult to free, having to shift the cut coal ever further behind them as they progressed and timber the roof as they went, the men achieved a phenomenal rate of progress, 7½ yards of advance per day. They would at first have been able to 'cast' the cut coal from hand to hand to clear the face of the working, but as it progressed a road would have had to be laid behind them. Add the difficulty of ventilating such a one-way passage without the aid of modern-day forcing fans, the natural urgency of the situation and the need for speed, but knowing that every day lost reduced the chances of finding anyone left alive on the other side of that mocking, challenging wall of glittering coal, you then have some inkling of the fantastic achievement of those unnamed, unknown heroes.

Chapter 11

RECOVERY

4th July

A time comes in every rescue operation, when either a successful result is happily achieved, or reluctantly, all hope of saving life must be abandoned, from that point onwards the entire operation has to be re-designated a Recovery. All urgency can be dropped, careful examination as to cause and effect, recovery of bodies and safety of the mine goes forward at a steadier, more safety-conscious pace, noting all details and forming a proper, "order of recovery". This is sometimes, understandably, difficult to fully comprehend.

Relatives and friends are naturally anxious and unwilling finally to accept the inevitable, they clutch at any straw, rumours abound and circulate quickly at such times. The target of their questions was almost always the tired, shaken members of the exploring teams. These grim-faced men, often badly affected by their experiences, were avidly sought out by press and public alike. Public relations were little considered, and reporters, starved of real news, often with little or no experience of the harsh realities of what life was all about in a mining village, wandered at will from group to group, often into the very homes of the bereaved, fuelling tension and anxiety with inane insensitive questions. Recovery had to be slow if lessons were to be learned, but the waiting was always resented.

We must now return to the day of the accident, and to the men left in the pit when the inrush finally sealed off the shafts. Three men, Francis Bradley, John Wilbourn and William Vernon were working on the northside of the pit, close to the barrier between No. 2 and No. 4 pits. They had a putter boy with them, William Holmes, aged 11. These were the men that the corporal, Benjamin Wright, had forgotten. They were driving an upward sloping heading and just before the flooding had been heard firing shots. These four were always presumed dead, as it was reasoned that the ventilation was shut off shortly after the shots were fired. Although the men would be out of reach of the water, it was thought that the fumes from the gunpowder would have killed them. (At that time the men supplied their own powder and fired shots themselves. Ordinary black powder was obtained from hardware shops and made into cartridges at home. Fuse was mostly made from straw filled with powder to entrain fire though the shot hole to the cartridge. There were frequent accidents, both to shopkeepers and miners but it took many more years before the practice was wiped out entirely.)

Joseph Cook, Alexander Bettison and John Carr worked in the stalls near to Dan's Incline and were under the care of a corporal named George Silkstone. Eli Forrester, George Mills, Thomas Wood, Joseph Wood, Joseph Hawley, Thomas Street, John Hill, Samuel Ashmore, John Buxton, William Wood, Thomas Brunt, Richard Siddons, Samuel Coates, John Butterfield and Reuben Jones all worked in the Dips, which was the district furthest from the shafts, under the control of an acting corporal, Thomas Britton. The last person lost was the aforementioned young boy, Joseph Ashmore, who on the day of the accident was greasing tub axles near to where the group of men were working.

Dip is a word which in mining can have two meanings, which although related, can be confusing. Most strata is inclined and that inclination can be observed, the observed inclination is termed *Indicated Dip*. Upon close examination it is often found that there is a greater inclination towards the strike, often very slight, which is the true angle of dip, this is termed *True Dip*. Suppose a situation where Indicated Dip is east and True Dip is N.N.E., then the lowest working will be at the furthest point N.N.E. Now suppose a fault which throws a seam downwards some way to the south, a greater distance than the depth reached on the True Dip. Any workings reaching this lower level, obtained by driving headings down into them, will be termed *Dip Workings*. In the context of our story the dip workings were to the south of Dan's Incline, but the shafts were to the north. As they were always set at the lowest possible level it must be assumed (dip is not indicated on the plan) that the dip workings referred to were situated at the bottom of some dislocation of the strata, a fault, but as the plan available is only a general plan of the mine, used to indicate points to a Coroner's inquest, and so not marked to avoid confusion, this explanation can only be assumed. Later in this story, in another incident, it can be shown by reproducing the plan that dip workings in that case refer to downthrow of the strata.

4th July

On the morning of 4th July 1861, a large party led by No. 4 pit overman, John Brown, went through the heading which they had completed in record time, just a few hours previously, and cautiously began to explore the northside workings. After examining the No. 2 incline and finding it free from gas and the ventilation flowing, they returned to the lower level which ran directly to No. 2 pit bottom. Here they were met by John Parker in company with a small team who had descended the shaft now that the ventilation was moving. The underviewer instructed them to continue along the level and they began cautiously inching forward until they too began to smell the sickly odour of decaying flesh.

After proceeding for 106 yards the faint light from their safety lamps picked out a small bundle of clothing lying piled up in the middle of the road, ten yards further on they found the naked body of young John Holmes, he was lying between the rails with his hand under his chin as if asleep! What horror must have filled the minds of those brave men, as they lifted their eyes from the dead boy and three yards further on beheld a naked man! Did hope spring in their breasts – could it be possible that someone had survived, yet could not bring himself to speak or to cry out to them? Peering closer through the gloom they saw that this man was a mass of bruises, he was standing almost erect, his back leaning against the road side. This was Joseph Wilbourn. Just beyond Wilbourn lay the bodies of Vernon and Bradley; both appeared to be sleeping. It was later reasoned that Vernon, Bradley and the boy had prepared to go to sleep and had lain down. The blackdamp had then moved into the mine, and being twice as heavy as air had first filled the low level of the road and overcome them immediately. Wilbourn had witnessed their deaths and appeared to have struggled against his own inevitable end. Unseen, but the experienced man knew well its deadly effect, the gas crept higher, until, perhaps driven insane by his frantic struggles, Wilbourn too perished, some time after his comrades.

On their way back to report to John Parker the explorers found the bodies of four horses. The first one appeared to have been strangled, it still had a length of chain wrapped around its neck. Both hind legs had been cut off and the legs placed in a tub, a small amount had been consumed. The other three horses appeared to have stifled to death from the effects of the gas. Coffins were brought into the pit and the bodies, liberally sprinkled with disinfectant, were taken out at 5.00a.m. the next day. This ended the recovery from No. 4 pit and Mr Hedley ordered the heading, driven with such high hopes, stopped off for the time being.

12th July
On 12th July, a further attempt was made from No. 2 pit. George Parker and Joseph Watts, overman at No. 2 iron-stone pit, leading nine others. They turned into the southside workings and worked their way along towards Dan's Incline. About 800 yards along the level they came to a large siding, where, lying in a tub, they found the body of Samuel Ashmore. His thirteen-year old son Joseph was found lying 20 yards further on. This was the boy who could have escaped but gave up his own life to warn his father. (At the inquest much was made of the boy's selfless act and his corporal was bitterly castigated for abandoning him.)

Two more bodies were found in the siding, Watts said later, that there was no sign of water, the men had made provision for a long stay, they had killed a horse and a few pounds of flesh had been eaten. Watts went on to give a clue to their deaths: "There had been blackdamp in the place; there were still traces remaining in the level when we entered." The bodies were very decomposed and the local policeman could not be induced to enter the temporary mortuary in the pit yard, to assist the identification. (In fact two men of this group were wrongly identified and buried under the wrong names.)

Shortly after leaving the siding, George Parker discovered the remaining bodies of a larger group. It would appear that, except for the men from the stone headings who were sealed up on their own, the rest of the men made their way to Dan's Incline, where, after seeing the settling waters, they decided to form two separate groups, the largest of which elected to stay near the water and watch for signs of it going down. The smaller, second group, taking most of the candles, seem to have elected to explore and perhaps find another way out. All lived for some time after the flood and had made provision for sustaining themselves, but perhaps it is right to assume, allowing for their proximity to where the gas entered the mine, that the larger group, near the incline, were the first to perish.

With this discovery and recovery of the bodies, the recovery operation at No. 2 pit was largely at an end. Now the engineers could examine the pit in detail, and the inquest, which had sat and been adjourned three times, could begin in earnest.

"Bringing up the first body".
Courtesy of Mr. J. Curry.

*Clay Cross
Company's No. 2
coal pit. Courtesy
of Cliff Williams.*

Chapter 12

THE INQUEST, VERDICT, AND AFTERMATH

1st August 1861

The District Coroner, Mr C.S.B. Busby, took the last of the evidence given in the inquest. It was to take eight full days, during which 73 witnesses were examined.

There are two versions of this inquest, which differ slightly on some very important points. The *Derbyshire Times* reported the hearing and this version can be found in the archives of the Local Studies Library at Chesterfield. The second version is the original shorthand transcript taken down and transcribed by Edward Blanchard, the coroner's clerk, who later produced a beautifully written, bound copy, upon which I have drawn heavily. This copy is now in the company's archives at Clay Cross.

Nineteenth century inquests were always painful affairs to the men employed in the coal mines. The men had little faith in them, the days were not then long passed since Lord Londonderry had instructed coroners in his vast northern coalfield, "Not to bother holding inquest over the body, if it be only that of a miner!" A 19th century miner's life was held a very cheap item. Trade Unionism was in its infancy, indeed many mining districts were still wholly dependent upon village sick-clubs and strictly controlled local combinations, low in funding and easily manipulated. Membership of the early mining unions was fiercely opposed by the employers (including the Clay Cross Company) and the men thought that inquest juries were little more than stage-managed affairs, consisting of members of the public, with little or no mining experience, owing suit to the local employer for their own livelihood. It was to be 21 more years, and Clay Cross would be once again in the spotlight, before the miners gained what they considered to be proper representation.

An example of the rumours which abounded at the time is contained in the opening statement by Mr Busby. After inviting the crowded public gallery to offer any further evidence, a woman stood up and said she had heard Dawes state that: "The water was running in to his stall at 11.00a.m. when George Parker and Smith were there, but that the Gaffer had threatened to fine Dawes if he complained". Dawes, Boden and Bradbury were all recalled and questioned on this, and all three denied the fact. Mr Busby then began the summing up of the evidence given.

First the coroner referred to the state and discipline of the mine prior to the accident.

After describing the general layout of the mine which has been recounted earlier, he went on to state the discipline. "John Parker is underviewer of the Clay Cross Company collieries, and has this, as well as others under his control. He examines different parts of the workings two or three times a week. Under him is his nephew George Parker, overman of the mine, who usually attends in the pit from 6.00a.m. to noon, and if anything should go wrong after that time the corporals report to his house. He goes to the company office every afternoon when Mr Binns is there, and also sees his uncle, John Parker, daily. He is assisted by his cousin Joshua Parker, who is called the deputy, who is in the pit daily. The mine is divided into nine districts, each of which is under the control and care of a corporal, whose duty is to care for his own district and to render aid to others in an emergency."

To the west of No. 2 Blackshale Pit were some old workings known as No. 1 pits, which had been abandoned for some years and were known to be full of water. There appears to have been a rumour among the colliers that some stalls, stopped in April, 1861, near Dawes' 177 stall, were stopped because of water, but the company proved that they were endangering buildings on the surface.

Dawes was criticised by the Coroner for not reporting the water, either to Alfred Smith or George Parker.

Samuel Bamford received similar criticism, for the coroner found: "You apprehended danger, and even fetched out your tools. You had seen the water, but you did nothing to warn others of the fact."

On the whole, he found the conduct of the corporals, with the exception of Alfred Smith, utterly abominable!

It became a painful part of the inquest to establish if any one of the men and boys, had lived for any length of time after being sealed up. Horses had been slaughtered, and parts of them had been consumed. Doctor Wilson, who examined the bodies, was of the opinion that the men had not died from starvation, or any other lingering death. They had all succumbed to the effect of Carbonic Acid Gas (blackdamp) and, as this gas is twice the weight of air, and many were found in a sleeping position, they probably died in their sleep.

Wilbourn appeared to have struggled against death, and from the condition and position in which his body was found had in all probability gone quite mad after the death of his companions.

Mr John Hedley had given evidence that he had been in the pit on several occasions and had never found any blackdamp. He advanced the following theory: "When the water broke into No. 2 pit it was followed by massive quantities of blackdamp from the old workings in No. 1 pit. For the three days following the accident the barometer had stood particularly low, and the atmospheric conditions aided the dispersal of the gas. When the exploring party went into No. 1 pit it was found to be quite free and I thought, upon reflection, that this was very unusual, as most old workings are usually full. I see now that the water, rushing into No. 2 pit, would have the effect of moving the gas, and the fall of barometric pressure would aid this movement."

The other mining engineers were in full agreement with this and the coroner accepted the fact.

The coroner found that Mr Binns' plan, and that of Robert Stevenson were accurate, and much play was now made upon the role of the unfortunate Martin (page 00), now long dead, and his uncharted heading and it was found that this work was in the very place where the water had burst through into 177 stall.

He asked the jury to consider seriously if any of the corporals were criminally negligent in their conduct and went on: "The whole case may be disposed of in the fewest possible words: is anybody responsible for any error in giving directions for the rescue of the men, or was any error committed in warning the men after the acccident occurred?"

Mr Abott (a juryman): "Are the company responsible for the negligence of their servants?"

The coroner: "Not criminally responsible."

The jury retired for two hours, then delivered the following verdict. "We find that the death of Francis Bradley and others, took place from the water accumulated in the No. 1 workings having broken in to 177 stall, No. 2 pit. There was not a sufficient barrier to keep out the water, in consequence of the coal in the deep No. 1 level having been worked for a distance of 42 yards beyond the south-eastern boundary shown on the working plan. But there is insufficient evidence to prove by whom, or under what circumstances, the coal was worked to beyond such boundary."

There is a strange anomaly here which bears examination and *should have done so at the time!* The working plan of the No. 1 pit was said not to include any evidence of workings to the deep of the old water level and yet John Parker had given testimony that *something which he saw upon the plan had drawn him to the place!* A plan was produced at the inquest (reproduced here) which shows all this alleged unauthorised work in perfect detail. It is given in evidence that the rotten roof in No. 1 pit would not allow entry into No. 2 when life was at stake, but are we to assume that somehow conditions altered so much that the inspector, or the company's surveyors could gain entry and produce such a detailed plan? Maybe the miners had a point when they complained about adequate representation!

The jury were of the further opinion that several of the corporals, viz: Thomas Britton, George Silkstone, Benjamin Wright and James Booth, were answerable for neglecting their duty under the Colliery Rules. They also found that the stallmen, Dawes and Bamford, were guilty of the same neglect. A recommendation was forwarded by the jury that in the absence of the ordinary deputy, a well-qualified person should be appointed.

The jury also recommended that all the old workings be drained, and that when a barrier is to be left, notice of intent should be served to the Inspector.

The jury further considered that there was great praise due to Alfred Smith for his exertions on behalf of men under his control.

The *Derbyshire Times* stated: "Alfred Smith and Thomas Boden were both recommended by the jury to the Royal Humane Society."

Upon delivery of the verdict, William Jackson Esq, addressed the jury and, repeatedly breaking into tears said: "On behalf of the Clay Cross Company, I cannot allow this meeting to depart without first expressing my deep regret, and that of everyone concerned, for the lamentable loss of life that has taken place. We feel that your verdict has, in public opinion, rendered us blameless. We have congratulated ourselves that under the management of Mr Binns, we had less loss of life than any colliery in the

Kingdom. It has ever been our wish to make the men in our employ comfortable, and ensure their safety. We hope that steps will be taken to ameliorate any suffering on the families who are bereaved, and I am sure that it will not be our fault. I hope that we shall never again be gathered here under such circumstances." That hope was not to be realised!

The District Inspector of Mines submits an annual report to the Secretary of State for Mines. The Report for 1861 is in part reproduced in Appendix I. It clears up some of the questions left unanswered by the coroner's inquest report into the innundation at the No. 2 pit, from which my story was largely drawn. Firstly, the inspector's report makes clear the fact that Martin was in fact the manager of No. 1 pit and that he operated under the direction of George Stephenson.

When the plan produced by the inspector is examined, it becomes clear to the eyes of any practical miner, that if the Original Mine Plan of No. 1 pit had shown the same detail, then John Parker had cause for concern when he had examined the plan all those years before (see page 00). A mining engineer, reading the available evidence and examining the plan, will at once recognise that what Stephenson and Martin were trying to achieve was simply a planned and well-executed Water Lodgement Area close to the shafts. What is not clear is how the water, once in the lodge, was to be pumped out again by a surface pump. There is no evidence of a pump facility installed underground which could either have lifted the water to a shaft-pump, or forced a head of water directly up the shaft.

The danger lay in the fact that what they were creating was, in effect, a sump. Properly recorded on the plan, the work would perhaps have caused a worry for the future, but the single heading where the breach actually occurred cannot be explained; it must remain forever a mystery, and it was probably a hint of this heading which drew Parker to it in the first instance.

With the exception of John Hedley's yearly report, this brought to an end, at least as far as officialdom was concerned, the final act in what came to be known as "The Clay Cross Calamity".

After the death of George Stephenson, his son Robert became the largest proprietor in the company. Robert Stephenson was also the Consulting Engineer to the London and North Western Railway. He found upon his return from Egypt where he had been examining the proposed Suez Canal, that a deal had been struck between the company and the railway that compromised his dual positions and he therefore resigned from the company. Ownership then passed into the hands of Sir William Jackson, Sir Morton Peto, and Sir Joshua Walmsley. For a fuller account of this the reader is directed to *The Midland Railway*, by F.S. Williams, 1877.

A point laboured at some length during the inquest, concerned the provision of basset shafts, or shafts close to the outcrop, up which trapped men could escape if the main shafts were cut off from them. This was taken to heart by the company, indeed by the mining industry generally. In the case of the Clay Cross Company this decision was to have a far-reaching effect in the future.

After the accident deputies were appointed, taking over the responsibilities formerly held by the corporals. A fund was started by the Lord Mayor of Chesterfield on behalf of the dependants. The Company subscribed £500 and Charles Binns £50. Sir William Jackson had stated that "Public opinion had rendered the company blameless". True or not, Charles Binns in reply to the Mayor's invitation to attend the meeting to launch the fund observed, "I hope you will accept my donation, but feel that it would be wrong for me to attend, *in the light of recent opinion!*" [author's italics].

The *Derbyshire Times* was also a little critical of the verdict. In an editorial to help to launch the Mayor of Chesterfield's appeal fund for the widows and orphans, the *Derbyshire Times* of 17th August 1861 injected a note of censure. Perhaps this was against the crop of rumour and counter-rumour which had flourished over the past two months, perhaps it also hinted at an awareness that the inquest findings had only borne out the worst fears of the men?

> "Whatever we may say or not say, think or not think about the cause of the Clay Cross Calamity, who was to blame or who was not to blame, we shall all agree on one important point, it is the widows and orphans of the unfortunate victims who now deserve our undivided attention and sympathy."

The Clay Cross Calamity

A weeping is heard, a loud lamentation
The sorrow so keen glooms over creation.
For death has deprived many homes of their stay,
The loving, the loved ones, have been swept away.

Oh sad was the stroke, the danger was fearful,
The rush of the waters pealed death in their roar,
And wild was the discord, not one eye looked
    cheerful,
For death in its gloom cast its shadows before.

Yes sad is the stroke, my husband is buried,
My father, my brother, are lost in the flood.
They perished as quickly they hurried to rescue,
Oh sick grows my heart and chill runs my blood.

Hush, stay the fond heart, and be not repining,
For providence works in mercy and love.
The soul of thy loved one e'en now may be shining
With glory refulgent in heaven above.

OMEGA

The 23 men and boys who lost their lives in the innundation
(listed in the order in which they were recovered):

Francis Bradley	Aged 41
John Wilbourn	Aged 38
William Vernon	Aged 34
William Holmes	Aged 11
John Cook	Aged 51
John Carr	Aged 25
Alexander Bettison	Aged 44
Joseph Ashmore	Aged 13
Samuel Ashmore	Aged 21
Samuel Ashmore	Aged 38
Reuben Jones	Aged 13
Thomas Brunt	Aged 32
Richard Siddons	Aged 26
John Butterfield	Aged 14
Eli Forrester	Aged 45
George Mills	Aged 24
Thomas Wood	Aged 61
Joseph Wood	Aged 19
Joseph Hawley	Aged 45
Thomas Street	Aged 69
John Hill	Aged 41
John Buxton	Aged 61
William Wood	Aged 38

Chapter 13

THE 1865 EXPLOSION

3rd May

Because it may help to better understand the following events, it is necessary to go a little deeper into the geology of the coalfield, more particularly, the geology of the blackshale seam.

The blackshale is really a number of seams, each sitting on its own seat-earth (the relic of the ancient carboniferous forest soil), in more or less close proximity. In some parts of the coalfield the whole sequence can be worked together, taking the seat-earths along with the coal; in other districts, because the bands of dirt, or coal, are thicker, this is not possible and some portions (termed leaves) are left behind unworked, these can be underfoot or overhead.

There are a number of economically viable seams below the blackshale horizon, which have been worked little at any great depth, except close to their outcrop, and mainly in the southern portion of the North Derbyshire Coalfield. In consequence the seams which lie beneath the floor of a blackshale pit have not been de-gassed, either by natural forces or by mechanical means, such as methane drainage. Furthermore, many of the interbedded shales and mudstones are carbonaceous in their nature, themselves containing small amounts of natural gas.

Over much of its worked area the seam is closely underlain by a strong gannister-like sandstone which, when pressure is applied from above (what the miner calls weight), tends to heave-up in large slabs and release huge amounts of gas (termed blowers), derived from unworked seams below, which have migrated upwards along natural breaks, or pressure breaks in the sub-strata.

Modern mining methods counteract this potential danger with a planned system of methane drainage carried out close behind the advancing face line. But in the 19th century it was never known from one day to the next when a sudden blower would erupt into the workings, turning a normally safe and adequate air-current into a highly explosive mixture.

The Clay Cross No. 4 Colliery, better known locally as The New Foundation, was sunk around the same time as the Nos. 2 and 3 pits. It lay north of the works yard, close to Clay Cross Station. It will be remembered that it was from this pit that the heading was driven to try to save the men trapped in the No. 2 pit in 1861. Although the heading was stopped-off after the rescue attempt, the modern British Coal plan of workings in the blackshale seam for the area shows four such connections were eventually made.

The blackshale seam was five feet thick in the No. 4 pit, which was laid out and worked on the same plan as all the other company pits of the time. (It may be of interest to note that these collieries were acknowledged Model Pits. An air flow of 6-7,000 cubic feet per minute was considered to be more than adequate, in fact, more than was necessary. A modern mine can receive up to half-a-million cubic feet per minute.) The ventilation was impelled by the usual underground furnace, the pit was considered to be generally free from gas. The District Inspector held all the company's pits in the highest regard, most of the men felt safe and quite happy to use candles in their work, the pit employed around 500 men and boys. The coal trade in the area was increasing and the *Derbyshire Times* was reporting almost full-time working in the pits again after previous decreases in local trade.

The early morning of 3rd May 1865 saw 20 men below ground in No. 4 pit. Moses Marriott the colliery engine-wright, was also hard at work. (My friends, Cliff Williams and John Robinson, well-known local historians, tell me that Marriott's name was probably Hosea. This is very close in pronunciation to Moses. However, Edward Blanchard, who also took the shorthand notes for this incident and produced a written longhand account, named him Moses. I have therefore stuck with his nomenclature as he was the man actually taking down the depositions.)

The winding engine had been giving some trouble and Marriott was anxious that his repairs and adjustments should be completed in the slack period of the back shift, or else the main coal-turning shift that followed would be disrupted. Like all his breed Moses was infatuated with steam engines. Nothing was too good for them, and time spent in loving care and attention to their needs and whims was time well spent. After all, the Owd Gaffer, the legendary Geordie Stephenson had been an enginewright just like himself, and look where dedication and application had taken Him.

At 2.00a.m. Marriott heard the ring of clogs crossing the pit yard. As the sound grew nearer he could just make out the shapes coming onto the bank. He knew them both very well; Thomas Bamford and John Currey were both deputies, Currey in fact was widely regarded for his pit-craft, known to management and men alike as the best and most experienced man in the pit.

Both were on the early turn. In those days it was the practice for the deputies to go below and examine the workings before the main body of the hewers arrived. They chatted briefly and then Marriott sent the two into the pit. Hardly had he shut off steam and begun some minor re-adjustment when the bell clanged again, this time from the pit bottom, signalling that riders were waiting to ascend. Marriott brought the cage to rest on its keps and released the night-shift deputy Richard Wilson, free, now that Currey had relieved him, to make his way home to nearby Furnace Hill and a warm bed, perhaps to be sound asleep before the dawn broke.

Marriott returned once again to his engine; it would be some time before he was disturbed again and he was anxious to complete his adjustments. (Under a three-shift system introduced much later, winding times for men riding were introduced and rigorously imposed; in mid-19th century practice the hewers tended to arrive in small groups. Coal was not wound during the night shift, except when an unusually high demand enforced it, and it was little trouble to regulate the winding speed to accommodate frequent man-riding in the shafts.) A train passed on the nearby railway as he paused to light his pipe; the time he noted was exactly 2.30a.m. A frown appeared on his face as an unfamiliar sound intruded upon his thoughts, a sound quite unlike the usual hiss of steam from the engine or the clatter of the train on the main line. This sound was different and he sought to assimilate it, the source became clear and the answer was all too horribly apparent as, with a sickening report, the ground shaking violently beneath his feet, the shaft vomited dense clouds of smoke from its mouth.

Moses Marriott had a lifetime of experience of collieries and their ways, he knew from bitter experience that there was little that he, alone, could do to bring aid to the men below ground. He immediately began to run up the main line towards Clay Cross, his path lit by the lurid glare from the furnaces, nascent transformation of one element by fire, whilst below their bellowing shaking foundations, fire was at that moment destroying life.

John Brown, who as colliery overman had done so much and laboured so hard, just four years earlier, to try and rescue the men trapped in No. 2 pit, was now colliery manager of the No. 4, and it was to his house that Marriott directed his steps. Brown sent him to alert the company engineer, William Howe, and as he hurried on, the worried enginewright noted that many people were up and about. Awakened by the shock-wave of the explosion, they were making their way to the works yard and the No. 2 pit bank, thinking no doubt that it was there that disaster had struck again.

Mere words cannot adequately describe a colliery explosion. For various technical reasons each is subtly different (the graphic illustrations included in these pages, may help to convey some understanding), novel-type accounts leave the experienced pitman shaking his head in disbelief, official reports, with all their weight of necessary technical details are hard and dry for the layman to follow. Below are two graphic, totally different accounts.

A little known volume, *Half Hours Underground*, has an interesting account of a lucky escape from an ignition in a mid-19th century mine which seems to have been, luckily, badly ventilated! "Under the guidance of the foreman we then set off on our tour. The main passage, along which we went at first, was what I imagine would be considered a lofty and spacious gallery, laid with rails, it was comparatively broad, and seemed to my eye about nine or ten feet high. We proceeded along this for, I daresay, a quarter of a mile.

By-and-by our leaders turned into an apparently unused side gallery, narrower than the main passage, in which the foreman had something about the ventilation to point out to the owners. Hitherto we had seen no men mining; we had met men with horses drawing trucks, and others going about their occupations, but no men working. We proceeded along this smaller gallery for about a hundred and fifty yards or so. The place was dirty, sloppy and wet, and of course, dark; and feeling no particular interest in what the foreman was desirous of pointing out to the owners, I lagged behind a little. I might have been twenty paces behind the rest of the party, when a sudden light started up among them − I can compare it to nothing but the flash of mimic lighting, with this difference, the light flashed up to the roof and assumed the mushroom shape, but it did not disappear. Instead of being extinguished as instantaneously as it arose, it continued extending and spreading out along the roof on every side.

My first idea when I saw the light was, that this was some civility on the part of the owners to show off the mysteries of the place to their visitors, as I had seen the Blue-John Mine in Derbyshire, and other stalactitic caves, illuminated by Roman candles and other lights. That idea only lasted for a second.

As the light extended, every one rushed panic-stricken from it as fast as they could run. I guessed the truth in a moment, and turned to fly. There was no difficulty in finding my way, the whole place being illuminated. After flying along for some time I looked back; the whole of the gallery where we had been was one body of fire – not a bright lambent but lurid, reddish volumes of flame, rolling on like billows of fiery mist. Their form was like that of the volumes of black smoke which we may see at times issuing out of large factory chimneys, more than anything else I can compare it to. My notions of explosions of fire-damp were, that they took place with the rapidity of an explosion of gunpowder. But it was not so in this case, at any rate. I do not mean that it was slow, but that its speed was no greater than that of a man. All those who were at the end of the gallery where it took place did, in point of fact outrun it. Neither was there any noise or sound of explosion; at least, I noticed none, and if there had been I think I must have observed it, for all things considered, I was tolerably collected. The report must have taken place at the pit-mouth, as from the mouth of a gun.

The fire rolled silently along in billows of reddish flame, one wave tumbling over another in quick succession. And a curious and a very beautiful thing were the edges of these billows; they were fringed with sparks of blue flame, dashed of like sparks from a grindstone. Even at that dreadful moment I could not avoid being struck by their beauty.

All this I must have gathered at a glance – in an instant of time. In front of the billowy mass of fire rolling on towards me I saw the dark figures of my companions tearing along at headlong speed. Then turning, I again dashed on. When I came to the loftier main passage I heard a voice behind me cry out, "Down on your face!" and by-and-by one figure after another sprang past me and dashed themselves headlong on the ground. I can liken the reckless, frantic way in which it was done, to nothing but boys, when bathing, taking 'headers' into a stream. Without reasoning about it I followed suit, and flung myself into a puddle, and then peering backwards under my arm, waited the approach of the sea of flame, the wall of fire, which was approaching. It had not yet come out of the side gallery, but the glare of its light preceded it.

Presently it rolled into sight, filling the whole mouth of the side gallery, from top to bottom. Had it overtaken us in it, not a soul would have escaped alive; but when it entered the larger gallery it lifted, just as one sees a mist lifting on the mountains, and then rolled along the roof, passing over our heads. How much space there was between us and it, I cannot say; I imagine it filled the upper two-thirds, leaving a space of, perhaps, two or three feet from flame. Nor can I well say how long we lay below this fiery furnace; it might have been five minutes or a quarter of an hour. Judging from our sensations, it must have been hours, but we did not experience so great a heat as I should have expected. We felt it more afterwards; probably the anxiety of the moment made us insensible to its intensity.

After the lapse of some time the volume of fire above began to diminish, the stratum got thinner and thinner; it eddied, and curled, and streamed about leaving the more prominent parts of the roof exposed like islands; then it wandered about like fiery serpents and tongues of flame, licking a corner here, or flickering about a stone there, but ever moving towards the shaft. As it thus abated, presently one head was raised from the ground, then another, until we all began to get up. We then gathered together, but there were no mutual congratulations, nor external acknowledgment of thanks to God, however much some may have felt. But I doubt if there was much feeling of that kind, the sense of peril was yet too strong; we had escaped one great danger, but we knew that we were still exposed to the risk of many others which often followed such explosions. The first danger was want of air; the fire had used what was in the mine almost wholly up, and we might perish from want of it.

We followed the foreman to some better part of the mine and while gathered there together a loud crack ran through the roof above our heads, which so alarmed the already nerveless miners that some of them actually sank to the ground... Although the explosion had travelled so deliberately when it passed over us, it had sufficient violence when it reached the shaft to blow the roof of the building adjoining the pit-mouth clean off... Alas! the meaning of the dull report, and the cloud of smoke, and the fragments of the building flying in the air, were all too well known in the neighbourhood... We escaped with only miraculously slight injury for men who had gone through an explosion of firedamp."

What the writer so graphically described was, in its initial stages at least, more an ignition than an explosion, compare it with the following account from the same period, of an explosion in a well-ventilated northern coal-mine. "The moment of ignition can be likened to the effect that would be experienced if one were standing in the barrel of a gun a millisecond after the hammer falls upon the cap. The speed and violence of a gas explosion is unthinkable. Rock has been seen to melt, the temperature was so great. The violence increases outward from the flash-point, the air current reverses as the explosion sustains itself with fresh oxygen, which itself allows the flame to traverse the mine workings."

The author of the first account had been extremely lucky, the burning gas had found enough oxygen to sustain flame, but not enough to raise it to an explosive mixture. When it came out of the side-road its speed increased enough to pass over them, but the mixture did not reach violent proportions until it reached the vicinity of the shaft, up which it then spent its force. In the course of a firedamp explosion coal dust can be raised in clouds. This dust is itself explosive and can, if flame reaches it, cause and sustain further, even more violent, explosions in a chain-reaction. The mine is left filled with afterdamp, combustibles such as the wooden props, wooden tubs, grease which abounded in 19th century pits, men's clothing and even the coal itself, burn on long after the initial flash. The ventilation is reversed, and air-doors are blown down. Sometimes the mainly wooden headframes over the pits were completely wrecked, denying access to or egress from the mine, and in the meantime, those, if any, who survived such horrors were choking to death in the afterdamp. It was into such an environment as this that John Brown had to lead willing volunteers, with no more aids to breathing than wet rags bound around their faces, to render what aid they could to the 20 men and boys in No. 4 pit.

Chapter 14

THE SEARCH, CAUSE AND INQUEST

4th May

John Brown and William Howe arrived in the No. 2 pit yard a little before 3.00a.m. They were met by a crowd of anxious relatives clamouring for information and were at least able to assure them that the explosion had not occurred in those workings. Hardly had Mr Howe finished this bald statement when a coal-blackened face appeared before him.

William Bower, who worked in No. 4 pit, had felt the shock of the explosion but had not experienced any of its effect. He was working near the re-opened connecting slit between the two pits and reasoned that his best means of escape lay in going through the doors and then to No. 2 pit bottom and from there to the surface.

Bower could give the worried officials very little information. He had been working alone, and had no knowledge of his workmates, but hoped that others might soon follow him along the same escape route. While Mr Howe questioned him further, Brown called for volunteers from the crowd to accompany him into the pit. As was always the case there was a willing press of hands to his request, and shortly after 3.00a.m. Mr Brown, with his overman and six colliers descended No. 2 pit, where they were to remain for much of the day.

As the party made their way towards the connecting doors, they were relieved to meet a group of eight men coming towards them. All had come from the No. 4 workings, they could add the information that the explosion had taken place deep inside the pit, in an area called The Dips (see page 54). The plane of the explosion had badly shattered the workings, but they could give no account of any of their mates.

As the party neared the deep workings, the violence and effects of the explosion became ever more apparent. Doors had been blown down, tubs overturned and wrecked, then they found the first victim. It was John Currey; his clothes were still smouldering and it was obvious that he had taken the violence full in the face! They hurriedly extinguished his clothes and covered the body. Hopes were now sinking of finding any survivors as they continued the search.

Upon entering the area known as the dips a sad sight met the dispirited group. A pony lay dead across the rails, still hitched to three full tubs. Slumped against the roadside where the force of the explosion had flung him like a rag doll, was the body of its young driver, a ten-year-old boy who was badly burned and mutilated. There was nothing that could be done other than cover the little body and press further on. At No. 2 stall a fire was raging. Brown decided that this must be dealt with before going any further. The ventilation had to be improved, and this was no easy task when all the regulating doors had been blown down, destroying the normal path of the air current. The men were being badly affected by the afterdamp and kept having to be taken into fresher air to recover. Brown decided that the remaining fires must all be extinguished and the ventilation at least partially restored before further investigation could take place.

It was late in the afternoon when Brown and his weary party returned to the surface. Charles Binns, and the district inspector of mines, Mr Evans, were anxiously awaiting them in the company office, where Brown now hurried to give them his report. He told the meeting, which included, at least for part of the time, the anxious relatives, that the fires were now all extinguished, the ventilation was flowing again with the erecting of temporary brattices which replaced the wrecked airdoors. After giving details of work done, Mr Brown told the senior officials and the inspector that eight bodies now lay in the pit and that from his cursory examination it appeared that the explosion had been a firedamp ignition, and that he believed that this had taken place in No. 2 stall, where there had been a great fire raging. (In a firedamp explosion, the violence expands rapidly away from the initial flashpoint; building in its effect as it goes, it is possible, by observing these effects to establish the actual ignition point.)

After consulting the colliery books, Mr Binns sent for one of the men who usually worked in No. 2 stall on the day shift. This man, John Springthorpe, told them that when he was last in the stall, the floor had sounded hollow when he rapped it with his pick, a normal precautionary measure when examining the workplace at the start of a shift. Mr Brown told the Inspector that, after they had dealt with the fire, he perceived that the floor, close to the coal face, had 'heaved up' and large cracks had appeared in it.

After further underground investigation by the senior engineers and inspector, the following conclusion was arrived at: "The explosion had occurred in the No. 2 stall of Clay Cross No. 4 Colliery. The gas had been emitted from the floor of the seam, as a massive discharge, or blower, and this gas had found ignition when it came into contact with the candle of Thomas Fox".

Early the next morning the bodies of the eight killed in the explosion were brought to the surface where they were wrapped in blankets, and hurriedly deposited in the company's mortuary for formal identification.

The List of the Dead

Thomas Bamford	Aged 47
Thomas Spetch	Aged 10
Frederick Lowe	Aged 17
Samuel May	Aged 42
John Currey	No age stated
Ralph Stokoe	Aged 49
Thomas Smith	Aged 12
Thomas Fox	Aged 43

The Inquest, again held before Mr C.S.B. Busby, was in the Public Hall, Clay Cross, on 9th May 1865. This time real fury was expressed at the composition of the inquest jury, and the men complained bitterly to the coroner. It is difficult to see how a jury of persons, totally disinterested yet possessing the mens' requirements in underground skills could have been found, but the men felt that they had a good point. After the inquest on the victims of the Innundation four years earlier, it was widely felt that the Inspector, in his evidence, had erred too much in favour of the company (see Appendix I). No rumours about actual conditions in the pit have survived the years, but evidence was given that gas had *never* been found in the blackshale seam (difficult to believe) and that blowers are unpredictable occurrences, whilst in retrospect, such an innundation of gas was obviously always a possibility. It is no surprise that the jury, after only a short deliberation, passed a verdict of Accidental Death, occasioned by an explosion of gas.

Largely forgotten in the scale of wider events, never classified a disaster (except to those involved and their families!) the explosion at No. 4 pit passed into history. Forgotten? Maybe, but it was not to be the end of the story of misadventures in the Clay Cross pits.

Chapter 15

THE PARKHOUSE EXPLOSION

7th November 1882

Two miles to the east of Clay Cross, is the village of Danesmoor. It is difficult today to see it as a mining village. The pit closed in 1962, and its waste heaps and surface scars were wiped away a few years later by opencast mining. The pit that once stood there provided work for generations of Danesmoor miners; it was the Clay Cross No. 7 pit, Parkhouse Colliery, fondly remembered locally as 'Catty Pit'.

Parkhouse was sunk by the Clay Cross Company in 1867, 185 yards deep to the blackshale seam and reputedly on the site of an old Norman manor house. The late Mr George Griffin in his 'A Norman Manor House' (*Derbyshire Archaeological Society Journal*, vol XL) has the following observation: "When sinking the shafts at Parkhouse, the sinkers passed through the foundations, and then a slabbed floor of what undoubtedly were the cellars of the hall, and little does the Parkhouse collier realise today, that during the first eighteen feet of his descent, he is in fact passing through the cellars of a Norman Baron."

The colliery was sunk following the company's expansion policies. Large quantities of coal were being consumed by the domestic market, which had now fully accepted the new coal. Some of the best portions of the seam are coking quality. These so-called 'crozzling' coals, 'soft coal' is a more apt description, could appear to have put out an ordinary domestic fire, the householder would shovel the mass out in disgust, whereupon it would immediately burst into flame as air was let in! The public did not yet understand these unusual qualities.

The company themselves were now requiring large amounts for their lime kilns and coke ovens. The lime kilns were particularly suited to consume the bright slack (small coal), which was a huge bonus to production. (The student of mining history will often come across references to men involved in disputes regarding the use of shovels in loading out coal from the stalls. Many collieries could not sell small coal and the miners were required to load coal with a fork or riddle, discarding the smalls into the waste. This was not just wasteful, it was a loss to production and an item for which the men were unpaid, a colliery with a ready sale or use for this coal had a valuable asset.)

The lessons learned from 1861 were not forgotten here, even the provision of a basset pit was made possible by the purchase of a small worked-out pit near to Clay Cross. Commonly called Flaxpiece Pit, this was to figure prominently in later events.

The colliery was considered, like all the Clay Cross Company pits, a model of its day. Ventilated by furnace, the only difference in its working practice was that the stalls were smaller (15 yards between the gates), the coal was worked on 'end' to obtain good lumps, methane was practically unknown and safety lamps were only employed in 'broken ground' (area close to, or within a fault where the strata are affected with natural breaks).

Direct control of the pit was in the hands of Mr G.W. Dunn, the senior underviewer, and the whole group of mines were controlled by a Certificated Manager, Mr Crowdace. There were eight pits in production at the time, and the workforce at all eight pits had been drawn from other areas.

Parkhouse Colliery (Catty Pit) shortly before its closure, 1962. Courtesy of Cliff Williams.

Chapter 16

BONFIRE NIGHT 1882

In 1882 Bonfire Night fell on Sunday and consequently it was decided that the celebrations would take place the following night. Promptly at 6.00p.m. on the 6th, the huge bonfires built around the district were lit, and the fireworks let off. Potatoes and chestnuts were roasted and handed around. Christmas was not far away, the pits were in work though some on short time, and everyone was in carnival mood. The *Derbyshire Times* had remarked only weeks before: "Tonnages are good in the district and the future looks assured".

Three men who worked in Parkhouse pit, were on their way that evening to the Public Hall in Clay Cross. They were members of a choral society, going along to practice for the forthcoming Christmas Show, which was held annually for the workers and their families. One of the men had a violin case tucked beneath his arm when he left the house at 7.30p.m. to walk the couple of miles into Clay Cross, giving himself plenty of time to arrive at the hall before the rehearsal began at 8.00p.m. James Sims had worked at Parkhouse for about four years. Before going there, along with his brother-in-law Joe Stone, they had both spent much of their working lives in the old Morley Park pit at Heage, the village where both men had been born. It must have felt good, even in the harsh times of Victoria's England, to be shot of that particular worked-out hole, its long, dripping levels, blackdamp-filled hollows and the ghosts of men long dead which were reputed to haunt the workings. To be housed in some degree of comfort with the pit almost on the doorstep, no longer in the cramped miners' cottages of Baker's Hill and Leam's Yard, with their almost total lack of amenities, no longer a weary tramp to and from the pit, often in muddy, dripping-wet pit clothes. They now worked in a new colliery, for an employer who seemed to care for the workforce and take some interest in their lives and welfare and had even, by 1882, conceded to the men's demands for union recognition and representation.

James noticed one of his young sons by the bonfire and called the lad to him. the lad, flushed with the excitement of the evening, enjoying himself with his friends, was disappointed to learn that his mother wanted him home. James noted the look on his son's face and whispered that there was bonfire toffee hidden in the pantry, a bedtime treat that he could share among his family. The lad took to his heels, then paused and looked back towards the dying embers of the fire; in the firelight he saw his father raise his hand and wave goodnight. It was the last act of his father's life that young James Sims saw him perform, but over eighty years later he still recalled it with vivid detail; the boy was in bed long before his father returned home, no doubt worn out by the excitement of the evening, and his father was on early shift down Parkhouse the next morning.

Early Morning, 7th November

Around 4.00a.m. on the morning of 7th November fires were being raked and stirred-up to boil kettles. Outside the smoke from the houses mingled with the leftover fumes of the bonfire. The morning was damp and chilly, it wanted some hours yet till full daylight. Men were filling tea-bottles to take along with them, tea was always the preferred drink in the days when water supply could not be trusted; not many would be taking food into the pit as most of them would be back on the surface again by 10.00a.m., today being a continuation of yesterday's 'Play Day' and only a portion of the workforce would be going in.

After banking the fires once more, the refilled kettles were placed to simmer gently on the hob, doors began to close quietly down the blocks and the streets began to echo to the sound of clogs stamping in the chill mist. It was not far to the pit, by 5.30a.m. the men were all below. Most of them would take the downcast cage if possible though when the pit was fully working this was not always available and the smoke-laden upcast had to be faced.

Over 70 years later, there was still a feel about these old pits on the coalfield never experienced in the more modern mines. The super-pits with electric winding, floodlit surface installations, neon lighting, skip winding and a large cosmopolitan workforce, never evoked the same feeling. It was a subtle blend of sensations, and strange dark shapes which loomed suddenly out of a misty morning. A hiss of escaping steam from some unseen bank of Lancashire boilers, tubs jolting together, the stink of a nearby waste heap, the breathy sigh of the engine, its gleaming magnificence sometimes glimpsed as you passed the enginehouse, saw the wires flying over the headframe and heard the banksman cry for 'riders'. Even the pit-bottom felt different, pony smells emanated from warm stables, mixed with warm air from the workings, fumes from shot-firing, feed bins, wet timber and fresh-cut coal, but above all you sensed the long history. Men had worked, lived, laughed and died there – just as they continued to do in the super-pit – it just 'felt' different!

Issac Stone, the night deputy, rode up the downcast shaft; he had seen the day shift into the pit and handed over to two incoming deputies, Joe Booth and Bill Nuttall. He was looking forward to a cup of hot tea in the surface cabin while he filed his report. Issac had been busier than usual that night, the other deputy had failed to turn in and he had examined the whole workings alone. He wearily deposited his lamp and lit his pipe, took down the barometer reading for his report book, and saw that it stood particularly low that morning, a fact which, as a good and experienced official, he carefully noted.

At 8.00a.m. the village was up and about; the school was open today and mothers were arousing children worn out by the previous night's activities. A little after nine, with them safely inside the little school, the women could turn their minds to housework and thoughts of midday meals, perhaps a walk to Clay Cross to the shops, or even a short gossip with a friend or neighbour. Many of these women, as indeed the men, were related. Often whole groups had come from other areas, had known each other all their lives, and were related by blood ties over centuries. They were born into coal, just as surely as their menfolk.

The mist began to thin, familiar sounds from the as yet unseen pit intruded, comforting in their regularity. The scrape and rumble of the sorting screens, the hiss of exhaust steam from the winders, adding more moisture to the already saturated air. Shops began to open, the first time for three days; there was much to be done yet, some of their husbands would have already left the stalls and would be out of the pit by 10.00a.m.

Bill Johnson was alone that morning. Bill was a young clerk employed in the colliery office to keep the books, record the tonnage, order materials and run messages between the pit and the works for the manager. He distinctly heard the bell clang three times, the signal for riders, and glanced at the wall clock opposite his chair; it read 9.45a.m. He heard the long drawn sigh of the engine, could just make out the greasy rope flying over the head-pulley and moments later heard the clack of the safety gate as the upcoming cage caught and lifted it. He saw Joe Stevenson the banksman let the first of the returning shift off the chair, and even before the men were off, the bell had clanged again for riders. Johnson mused that, at this rate, the men would all be out by 10.00a.m.

In the village school the teacher was struggling with an arithmetic lesson, his charges still half-asleep. His eyes roved over the boys "How many of these boys would eventually find employment in Parkhouse pit?" he mused.

At Park House, the residence of the senior underviewer, Mrs Dunn was brewing strong tea, her husband, George, was upstairs in bed where he had been laid up for the past two weeks; this weather was no good for pitmen, they needed fresh clean air, not these miserable damp days. She sighed and took the cup up to him, observing that it was 10.00a.m. and her boys would be home soon. Mrs Dunn had four sons down Parkhouse pit that morning.

Cage arriving at the pit top (Downcast Shaft), Clay Cross Colliery. Courtesy of Cliff Williams.

Back at the pit, Johnson moved to the fire and checked the simmering kettle. The deputies would be in shortly with the reports, and his life would not be worth living if hot sweet tea was not ready and waiting for them. Miners' humour, rough, even coarse at times, but never ill-intentioned, is never so sharp as when it is directed at some minor official, and Johnson had suffered much, the butt of many a joke and quip from the good humour of a man returned to daylight and safety. It was to be many a long day before another such joke was cracked in this office!

The hands of the clock stood at 10.12a.m. Through the window he saw Stevenson standing tall and thin, beside the empty cage. Johnson was certain that the banksman never touched the signal bell, but at that precise moment the chair began to lift into the headgear! The banksman too took flight; Johnson watched in amazement as he flew through the air, completely off the bank, to land, fortunately, in a large open culvert which carried surface water down to the nearby river. The next moment the headframe splintered to match-wood, the ground heaved and trembled, and a huge cloud of dust and smoke vomited from the shaft. At the same instant the schoolmaster and his class felt a violent earthquake. Although he later said that he was at a loss to explain the cause, the children with pit-knowledge bred into them had no doubts, they flew to the window.

Chapter 17

7th NOVEMBER

10.15a.m. to 10.00p.m.

Bill Johnson was at a loss, the earth had stopped shaking and the terrible report of the explosion was beginning to clear from his shocked ears. Debris was still raining down in the yard and on the cabin roof. Men already at the surface, some walking down the pit lane, came running back. One did not bother to retrace his steps, he knew full well the scene, and instead began to run towards the main works; he knew that the shock and noise would have been heard there, but someone still had to report the source. Someone else ran towards Park House to alert George Dunn. Men working in other pits felt the shock-wave travel through the strata and made their way to the surface. The whole neighbourhood had felt the shock and waited with bated breath for the first report.

On the bank at Parkhouse, the boilers fell from their saddles, spilling hundreds of gallons of boiling water and venting scalding steam; the boilerman was badly scalded, and Stevenson too was in urgent need of medical attention. Horse-drawn ambulances were already on the way, and before midnight the little hospital at Clay Cross would be filled to capacity with their cargo.

Smoke, dust and fumes were now pouring from the mouth of both shafts and to the experienced officials just arrived from the works it was apparent that no entry could be attempted from there. They quickly retraced their steps, hurrying back towards Clay Cross and the old Flaxpiece pit, which had so providentially been linked underground with the Parkhouse workings in the event of just such a happening as this. It was upon this little shaft, not even provided with a steam engine, but only a horse-gin, that the eyes and hopes of the country would now be directed, as the flight began for the lives of the unfortunate men now trapped below.

Telegrams sped over the wires between Clay Cross and Derby. The senior Inspector of Mines, Mr W.T. Evans, and his assistant Arthur Stokes were informed.

George Dunn was hastily roused from his sick-bed and joined the huge crowd which soon gathered around the Flaxpiece pithead. Thomas Crowdace (general manager) organised a search party consisting of himself, Mr Dunn, J.Booth, J. Foster, P. Vardy and James Dunn, accompanied by two doctors, Dr Peglar and Dr Chawner, the works doctor.

Flaxpiece pit was not of course fitted with cages; a simple 'kibble', or iron bucket had to suffice, and into this the men now jumped to be lowered into the pit to begin a cautious examination of the workings. Meanwhile at Parkhouse, where another large crowd had gathered, some men had ventured close to the shaft and one thought that he could hear voices calling from below. Silence was called for and the men at the surface shouted loudly down the shaft. Back came a faint reply, "There are two of us, we have come from the workings and we have no light, send us down a light!" (These men had quite an adventure, their story is told later.)

The two men were told to stay where they were. Because of the danger of further explosions they could not risk sending them a light, instead a runner was despatched to Flaxpiece to inform Mr Crowdace, but when he arrived Crowdace and the search party had already departed underground. The man did not hesitate, only procured himself a lamp and leaped into the bucket to follow them with his urgent news. A few moments later a grim-faced collier emerged calling urgently for brandy! He informed the waiting crowd that the searchers had penetrated the Parkhouse workings and found the first victims. "Go and tell Mrs Dunn that her two boys are safe; they are injured and Mr Dunn is caring for them". A cheer was raised at this news, and brandy was soon pressed into his hands. Hardly had the bucket departed than it was landed once more. This time it was the manager Mr Crowdace, the pit was full of afterdamp and he had been overcome. Soon afterwards Dr Chawner was also brought out in a very distressed state.

At 11.30a.m. Thomas Crowdace issued a statement to the people gathered around the pithead. "We have made a preliminary investigation of the roadway leading to No. 7 pit. At the present moment the air is very foul with afterdamp, and flying around the workings are flaming blasts of air! We can do no more at this stage until the ventilation improves. It is believed at the present time that 30 persons are in the workings, but as quite a number of men working here do not live in company houses, this number could be more. Twelve of the 30 men so far accounted for are married".

Three hours later a further attempt was made to get through the workings to the bottom of Parkhouse shafts. At 7.30p.m., after the rescue party had been down for 5½ hours, the bucket was hoisted from the pit bottom, a few moments later a weary member of the team, gasping in the cold air, spoke to George Howe (son of William Howe company engineer), who immediately called for the ambulance. The bucket was sent down again and some moments later, as it began to rise, cries of distress could be heard in the shaft. As the bucket was landed, it was seen to contain William Dunn, son of the underviewer; he was badly burned and in great pain. The ambulance had only just departed to carry him home when the bucket landed once more. This time it carried a rescue worker supporting the head of Robert Dunn; the young man showed no sign of life and was severely burned and injured. Robert was taken home to Park House. William, who was only 16, died some days later from his burns.

By 9.00p.m. the rescue party were all back at the surface, sipping hot rum and recounting the horrors that had met them, one told a *Derbyshire Times* reporter: "After we got along the level, we came near to where they are building a new engine house [for an underground haulage engine], close to the pit bottom. [The party had got into the Parkhouse workings, entered the long escape level between the two pits, and got close to the bottom of the Parkhouse shafts.] Here I saw the bodies of the two bricklayers Slinn and Wheeldon. I also saw the bodies of Joseph Dunn, Richard Dunn, Michael Parker, Edward Barker, Henry Beeson and Joseph Phipps. [The two Dunns were George's eldest boys.] The bodies were blown in all directions, most of them had their heads down, as if they had tried to bury them in the dust. Close to Henry Beeson there was a pony; it was alive but badly burned. Next we went into the stables where there lay three or four horses badly singed. I looked in the pocket of one of the dead men; his watch was still going and the time was then 3.15p.m. We laid out the bodies where they were found; they had been blown about with great force. The Gaffer's Cabin, near the pit bottom was completely wrecked and in the wreckage we found the body of James Parker and also Mr Dunn's two sons Robert and William, they appeared to be asleep. The main road leading to the deep workings appears to be blocked by falls of roof, and these will have to be cleared first."

By this time it was becoming clear to the officials that there were far more men in the pit than they had first thought; the death toll was not known with any certainty and was set tentatively at 39. There was little check made on who went underground in 19th century pits. In this case, all that could be done initially was to send around the company houses asking who was missing! The men did not all take out numbered safety lamps and there was no motty system to give an accurate count. (A motty is a numbered brass disc handed to a banksman or onsetter when shaft riding. Properly done, the system gives an accurate picture of who is in a mine at any time.) The problem facing the officials was that all the men did not live in company houses, it was not certain how many had been asked to work that day, and there was always the possibility (all too real in this instance) that a stranger would be taken down for a look around with a view to induce him into regular employment.

Cage arriving at the pit top at Parkhouse (note the gentleman in smoking cap and carpet slippers, Mr George Dunn, Senior-underviewer, Clay Cross Company, who lost three sons in the explosion). Courtesy of Cliff Williams.

No. 124. **ARRIVAL AT DAYLIGHT.** [See No. 120.
Pony arriving at the top of the shaft after nearly 20 years in the bowels of the earth. Ponies not infrequently spend nearly the whole of their lives underground. This photo was taken at one of the Clay Cross Mines where the celebrated "C.X.C. Gold Medal" Coal is produced.

Chapter 18

THE TWO WHO ESCAPED

In the little hospital at Clay Cross lay two men, Aaron Topliss and Joseph Buckland. Both were suffering from the classic symptoms of carbon monoxide poisoning; violent headaches, sore throats and swollen tongues. That the pair were alive at all is greatly to be wondered at. These were the two men who earlier in the day, had called up the shaft at Parkhouse asking for a light. Topliss told George Howe: "We went down the pit as normal, we were working in a stall in the South Workings. We worked away without interruption until 12, or 1 o'clock and were unaware of anything unusual at all.

About this time a man named William Wildman came into our stall. He was opening out a stall on the same road, but closer to the pit bottom. He asked us if we had noticed anything wrong with the ventilation, and we told him that we had not. Bill was a bit upset, because he said that some time ago the ventilation had stopped when he was out in the gate, he went back into the stall-road, but when he came out again he noticed that the air had reversed, it was now flowing in the opposite direction.

We were using safety lamps; this is a part of the pit which is new and you could find gas. After Bill left us we decided to come out, up until then we had not noticed the air. Joseph hitched four tubs of coal onto the pony, we started to make our way to the pit bottom. We made about a hundred yards towards the shafts when our lights went down! Mine which was trimmed down anyway, went out. There was a queer smell in the air, rather like a match burning [the smell of afterdamp]. We went a few yards further but the air was getting worse so we turned back. We got as far as the big siding, on the road to the pit bottom [about 500 yards from the shaft]. There were a lot of tubs lying around, some with their wheels blown off. We next tried on the High Level, but after we got to the shaft, we decided that there had been an explosion! and we could not get out that way. We came back to the big siding and were making our way towards Flaxpiece pit when we heard voices, we then saw the lights coming towards us."

Topliss's own words are graphic enough; they need no further comment. When the rescuers found them they still had the pony, and the four tubs of coal with them, even though, at long last, the truth of their situation had dawned. Their lips and tongues were so swollen they had difficulty in breathing; they could hardly walk and were put into tubs to be conveyed to the pit bottom. They had been extremely lucky; the afterdamp, which Topliss so graphically described, had been partly diluted by the time they decided to come out of the stall. They were lucky to be alive.

The account is also of interest as it shows the vagaries of an explosion, some parts of the pit being blown to bits while others were hardly affected. Pits miles away felt the shock of the ignition, these men in the South Workings felt nothing! Even the reversal of the air current meant little to them initially.

7th to 8th November, 3.00a.m.
At 11.00p.m. on Tuesday night a further party went down into the workings. They carried large wads of cotton wool which the doctors said would give them some protection against the afterdamp. When volunteers were called for, 70 to 80 men stepped forward. The party was led by Mr Laverick (manager of Riddings Colliery), Mr Mills (of Coke and Mills) and Mr Heston (Staveley Iron and Coal Company).

With some difficulty they managed to clear a way through the worst of the roof falls and gained entry into the deeper regions of the pit. The roadways were covered with a thick layer of fine coal dust and they noted that along the path that the explosion had followed fine dust, which would have been raised by the blast of the pressure wave, had been converted into coke by the terrific heat of the flames that followed.

Leaving the main path of the violence, they ventured into some of the stalls; the air was still very foul in many of these places and it was only with difficulty, and supreme courage that 15 more bodies were discovered. Here the damage was not so marked, these men seemed to have succumbed to the afterdamp; many were fully dressed and had no doubt been making their way out when the air reversed, bringing the poisonous fumes to them. The team could do little but chalk the bodies, giving each a number which would be helpful when a more detailed examination took place, and carry on with the search, the bodies were, for the time being, left in the pit. (During the recovery stage later, the position and effect upon the bodies would be noted and entered on a plan, but this was not the function of a first search party.)

At dawn the next day, the whole area presented a miserable face. The reporters were around in force, wandering between Flaxpiece and Parkhouse, garnering such information as they could. The *Derbyshire Times* reporter said: "The pit head this morning was a very sad sight, a vast crowd having been gathered there all night, trying vainly to obtain further details. There are a great many blinds drawn this morning, both in Clay Cross and Danesmoor, and people are frantic for news!" They would gain very little in the way of fresh information for some time, the rescuers had been back at the surface since 3.00a.m. and no further work in the pit had been ordered.

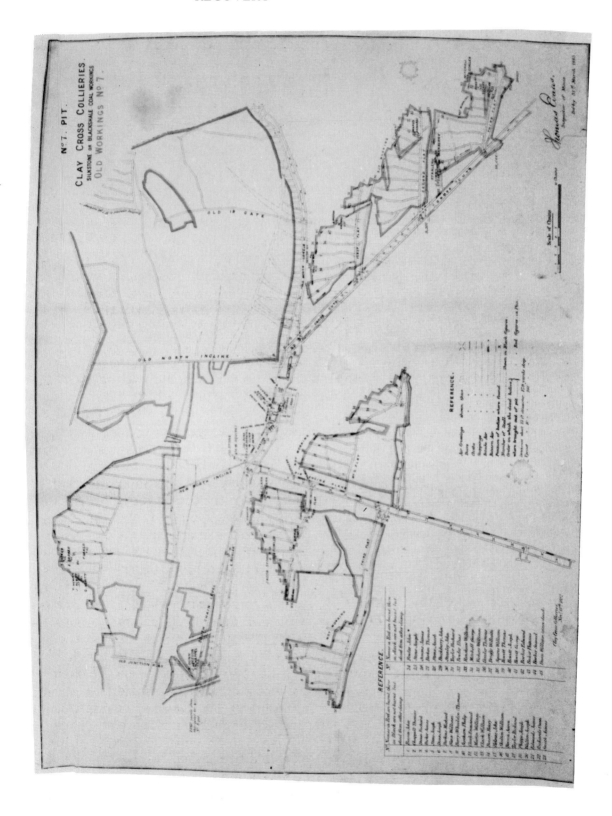

Chapter 19

RECOVERY

Mr J.P. Jackson, manager of the Clay Cross Company, arrived at the works office a little after 8.00a.m. on the 8th, and went into immediate and urgent consultation with the senior officials. One person missing from the meeting was George Dunn. Worn out by his exertions, saddened by the news of what had happened to his own decimated family, the underviewer was back in his sick bed, and Mrs Dunn had also two very sick sons to attend. Happily for the Dunn family, young Robert, although badly burned, survived but his brother William died on the night of the 8th.

Thomas Crowdace, recovered from the effects of the after-damp, attended along with George Howe, Mr Dickenson who had charge of the operation from Flaxpiece pit, and the managers of Grassmoor, Riddings and Wingerworth collieries were also present, along with the Superintendent of Police Their first task was to try to sort out the Order of Recovery, which was all that the operation could now be; life was extinct in the pit, the rescue operation was at an end. It is necessary to learn from all accidents, and on-site examination of the bodies was vitally important to learning the cause, whereabouts and path of the explosion. Also, over 40 bodies lay in the pit. These had to be recovered, received, cleaned and laid out for identification, coffined and eventually buried, the whole of the operations being carried out with as much decency and respect as possible. The doctors had to examine the bodies of the victims, details would be required later by the Coroner. Not all the men had died from burns, and the precise nature of their deaths had to be determined. This is what is meant by an 'Order of Recovery'.

A telegram arrived, informing the meeting that the Inspector and his assistant would be coming shortly. The meeting decided that a start could be made to recover the bodies from the pit at 2.30p.m. (I checked the newspaper account of this

Opposite: Plan of Parkhouse Colliery workings, produced at the coroners inquest, November 1882, showing positions of the bodies. Courtesy of Cliff Williams.

statement, it seems incredible that the most highly respected of all the Derbyshire Inspectors, Mr Evans and Mr Stokes, were not available until 24 hours after the greatest tragedy from explosion in the history of the coalfield? But that is what it says.)

It was thought best to deposit the bodies in a large club-room at the rear of the Queens Head, in Thanet Street, near to the Flaxpiece pit, rather than bring them through the town. From 2.00p.m. onwards and throughout the day, a mournful crowd saw the canvas-shrouded bodies slowly emerging from the pit. By 10.00a.m. Thursday morning, 15 had been brought to the temporary mortuary where, along one wall were ranged a huge stock of hastily constructed coffins. A number of women now gathered up the bodies to lay them out for inspection.

Courtesy of Cliff Williams.

The Cemetery Entrance, Clay Cross

POST CARD.

PRINTED IN GREAT BRITAIN.

For INLAND Postage only the space may be used for communication.

The Address only to be written thereon.

Fern Cottage,
CLAY CROSS.

Dear Sister,

This Monument was erected in 1883, in Memoriam to 45 Men & boys who were killed by a pit at Clay explosion at one of the C.X.C.º pits in Novr 1882.

Yours faithfully,

J.W. Bra...

Young William Dunn had died during the night, bringing the death toll up to 45. Sad tales were related to the ever-present reporters who mingled with the relatives, these are just a sample of their accounts.

James Parker had been working on the day of the accident with young George Dunn, constructing the engine house where the two bricklayers had died. Parker had only gone to work that day in great pain from an accident the previous day in order to supervise the bricklayers.

Then there was the poignant tale of the unnamed butcher's boy. This lad had been employed by a Clay Cross butcher, but desired to go down the pit to work with his mates. On Tuesday morning they took him along with them to see if he would like it! He lay with them now, at the rear of the Queens Head, they would be together for all eternity. Strangely, a similar type of explosion occurred two years before this, at Seaham Colliery, County Durham, again with large loss of life. One of the victims was a young butcher's boy who had gone with his mates to see if he would like the work.

Phineas Baker had previously served with distinction in the Marines, when Victoria's navy ruled half the world. Shot, storm, disease nor savages could quell Phineas; he came back to die in a Derbyshire coal-mine.

Perhaps the saddest of these tales, was not related until 29th November, after the victims had all been buried. The *Derbyshire Times* reported:

"Mrs Ann Beeson lost her husband and two sons in the explosion. She attended them at the mortuary, washed and cleaned them, and saw them buried. On November 24th, the poor woman gave up the struggle, perhaps she no longer wished to live, she died of a broken heart".

Another victim of Parkhouse.

*Inscription on the
memorial in Clay
Cross cemetery*

THIS MONUMENT
IS IN MEMORY OF THE
FORTY FIVE MEN AND BOYS
WHO LOST THEIR LIVES IN AN EXPLOSION
AT PARK HOUSE PIT, CLAY CROSS,
NOVEMBER 7TH 1882,
AND WAS ERECTED BY THEIR
FELLOW WORKMEN
AND THE
PUBLIC
1884.

Chapter 20

THE INQUEST

Mr Busby was once again the Coroner. The inquest opened at the Queens Head at 2.30p.m. on Thursday 13th November, as the bodies were still being brought out of the pit.

The jury were sworn and then went to Park House, the residence of the underviewer, to view the body of William Dunn. By the time they returned 24 bodies were ready for inspection. The coroner said he was only going to take evidence of identification at this stage, he warned the jury to be ready at all times to meet further corpses as they were brought out of the pit. He then bound them over in the sum of £40, and took the evidence of identity, afterwards adjourning the inquest until 22nd November.

The day following this first session of inquest, the colliers held a meeting of their own at the Angel. They strongly objected to the composition of the jury, and passed a resolution: "This meeting thinks the men on the jury are not capable of dealing with questions arising from the explosion. We further desire to have an inspection of the workings conducted on our behalf."

It was agreed to ask Mr James Haslam of the Derbyshire Mineworkers Association to conduct the inspection, and also to represent them at the inquest. There are a number of points of interest here. As has been shown earlier, the miners were always highly suspicious of inquest juries, and up to this point had always failed to secure representation on their behalf at inquests. The newly formed Derbyshire Mineworkers Association was now respected and had gained muscle power, mainly through the leadership of men like Haslam, a local man who had in fact once worked as a hewer at Parkhouse. It was to be the first time that the Union had ever represented the men at such a hearing. They were on firmer ground in requesting inspection of the pit on their behalf, as it was now covered by law that workmen's inspection should take place. In theory the employers could have objected to Haslam, but there was little to hide anyway, and he was highly popular with the men, who trusted him completely.

The jury consisted of:

A. Linacre	Gentleman, Foreman
L. Wigley	Butcher
W. Wiser	Blacksmith
A. Hanson	Draper
C. Hayes	Builder
W. Slack	Butcher
H. Clayton	Grocer
A. Milner	Farmer
H. Brakes	Plumber
W. Coldron	Licensee
J. Unwin	Dealer
S. Leafe	Grocer
J. Udall	Draper
J. Thorpe	Butcher

In the midst of all this controversy, the recovery work went on. The Parkhouse headgear was restored and the cages put back in the shaft. The day following completion of this work the pumps were put to work, and the Assistant Inspector Arthur Stokes, made his first official inspection of the workings. He first visited the Cross Cuts, where the explosion was thought to have originated, and then proceeded to other parts of the mine. His careful examination took four and a half hours and, perhaps understandably, he declined to reveal any significant facts on emerging.

On Monday 20th November a large crowd gathered at Parkhouse, when it was learned that James Haslam was about to conduct his own investigation on behalf of the workmen. He was accompanied by three very experienced men, Mr Downing of the Derbyshire Mineworkers Association (treasurer), Joseph Foster, and John Macey. With these men, the locals felt, they would get fair and honest representation of the facts.

(It may help to follow these two inspections, to imagine three steps. The tread of each represents a Flat. The flats were caused by natural faulting of the seam which was thrown down successively. The Cross Cuts were driven down across the faults to reach the seam at its lowest unbroken level.)

They went through the old stalls in the North Incline and

found them to be in perfect order, the roof sound and the timbering perfect, with not a trace of gas. They next went south-east into the Cross Cuts, going to the bottom of the third, or last, flat, and then working their way back up. This was the area where the full force of the explosion had been felt. Some old pillars had been entirely removed and there were huge cracks in the floor. In one stall a huge break in the roof was also noticed. Mr Haslam told the expectant, waiting miners: 'Although we cannot say the gas exploded there, it is very probable that the gas came from the Cross Cuts."

The District Inspector Mr Evans, then conducted his own inspection, along with his assistant Mr Stokes, Thomas Crowdace, and Mr Laverick. They went straight to the Cross Cuts, but he declined to give the results of his inspection when they returned to the surface.

The Coroner resumed the inquest on 22nd November, at the Victoria Hall. Thomas Crowdace was the first witness to be called. Some of the points raised are of interest here and worth repeating. There were 250 men employed at the colliery, of which 200 were coal-getters. Thirty-six horses were used for haulage, of which five were killed and one was later destroyed. The workings dipped very much near to the pit bottom, here he produced a plan, reproduced here, which showed the workings and the positions of the bodies. He also produced the deputies' report books, which showed no trace of gas found on previous shifts.

James Haslam was afforded every opportunity to give evidence, and also to cross-question witnesses. Mr Evans and all the other mining engineers were of the opinion that the explosion was the result of a sudden blower or feeder of gas, originating in the Cross Cuts, or near to the bottom flat, finding ignition at the flame of a candle. (The candle was thought to have been that of Joseph Stone.) The jury could do little but record a verdict of Accidental Death, for which no one is to blame.

Most of the unfortunate victims of the Parkhouse explosion were buried in the Clay Cross and Danesmoor cemetery, the large graves can still be found today. William Dunn was buried privately, and the three Heage men came home to the village of their birth. A Heage diarist, Joseph Wright, himself a miner and active union man (for which the Butterley Company had placed him on a permanent blacklist), states that there were in fact six Heage men killed in the explosion, the others were: Jacob Stone, a second Joseph Stone, and a man named Shelton.

The plaque on the monument, just inside the cemetery gates, reads: – "This monument is in the memory of the 45 men and boys, who lost their lives in an explosion at Parkhouse Pit Clay Cross, 7th of November 1882, and was erected by their fellow workmen and the general public 1884".

There is little to add, life goes on. Pits continued to blow up, to take fire, flood, close down, re-open, or simply fade from memory. The beautiful and simple Durham Miners' Memorial in Durham Cathedral, quotes a passage from the book of Job: "They are forgotten of the foot that passeth!" This writer hopes that this little effort will help to ensure that the 76 men and boys who perished in the Clay Cross Calamities, and the hundreds of others who died less publicised but no less tragic deaths over the long history of Derbyshire's coalmining industry, are never forgotten.

Chapter 21

REFLECTIONS

The British coalmining industry, what there is left of it, led the world in technology and experience. That experience was hard won, it came from the sacrifice of lives, not just the publicised sacrifices of large disasters, but more from the untold thousands of miners who died unsung, mundane forgotten deaths, callously written off because, "It was only to be expected of a miners lot". But was it, did it really have to be like that? Perhaps it really did take disasters to change things, if so, did all those thousands die in vain?

The coal industry is governed by a Coal Mines Act, by special regulations, and at local level by Managers' Rules. All that legislation came about as a result of bitter experience, it took time, thought, endeavour and guts, not only by miners, but managers, employers, scientists, politicians, small men, big men, all played their part in making the British mining industry the best in the world.

With the benefit of hindsight it is easy to say that the Clay Cross incidents need not have happened, that all three were foreseeable, that technology already existed that should have guarded against them and, contrary to the findings of the juries, someone was to blame! Unfortunately life is never that simple.

It is almost a paradox that such incidents should have happened in pits devised and laid out by George Stephenson. The best mining engineers of the day advised him, his pits really were models to be proud of, and perhaps, most ironic of all, George Stephenson perfected the safety lamp that would have prevented two of those incidents!

Only two generations ago, men of my grandfather's generation still persisted in using candles for illumination. Worse still, at Clay Cross on 9th December 1882, only one month after the Parkhouse explosion, the men at No. 2 pit struck from work. The reason? The company had withdrawn the right to use candles underground and instructed the men to take out safety lamps! Fortunately the men saw sense and returned to work the following Monday. The layman may find this fact unbelievable, that men would be so obtuse that they would risk life and limb simply to use a naked flame, but of course the real reason is much more complex.

The lamps invented by Sir Humphrey Davey, Dr Clanny, and George Stephenson, enabled the miner to carry flame illumination, with some degree of safety. They were not infallible, they gave poor light, and as poor lighting cost more lives than ever explosions did, the early safety lamp did not improve the situation but rather exacerbated it.

A modern miner's cap lamp gives an illumination of around 5 candlepower, weighs from 5 to 6 pounds, is carried on the belt and the helmet leaving both hands free at all times, and the light is directed wherever the user desires to look. The best of the workmen's flame safety lamps (in use from around 1911) gave a lighting of at most 2 candlepower, and even the best of the pre-1900 lamps would not give a whole candlepower. Lamps such as the Davy and Stephenson's Geordie, gave less than a third of one candlepower.

The hewer was the man, literally at the pick-point. He lay on his side in cramped unnatural positions and physically wrenched the coal from the ground. His eyesight determined not only his production rate, it also determined his life. He needed the best lighting conditions that he could obtain, and in the 19th century those were supplied by the humble candle. Hundreds of hewers died and probably never knew what hit them! They knew the risks, they accepted the odds, *because there was nothing better!*

JOHN HEDLEY'S REPORT, 1861

"No. 21 accident. Inundation of water, Clay Cross.

The accompanying plan shows the position of the workings inundated, No. 2 pits; also those from which the water came, No. 1 pits, which were made about 23 years ago. On the deep of No. 1 pits, and at that time up to the boundary, the late Mr G. Stephenson gave instructions to the manager of the pits, Mr Martin, since dead, to work out the coal within the letters A,B,C,D, for lodges for water. Five headings were driven to the deep, according to distances supplied to Martin, and a communication was made on the level course along the deep extremity of these headings. When this was completed, Mr Binns (now chief manager), at that time Mr Stephenson's private secretary, surveyed round these headings and laid the survey upon the plan. The accompanying plan represents that part of the workings as laid down on the plan. Martin was the responsible manager of the mine under Mr Stephenson's directions. Martin was instructed to get the coal out within the limits A,B,C,D, up to within 30 yards of No. 1 main level (note, 30 yards to the deep). Mr Stephenson had great confidence in Martin, and frequently left him for weeks together in charge of the works. At this time Mr Stephenson was very much from home with his professional engagements, Mr Binns also accompanying him.

In 1848, the No. 1 pits ceased coal getting, and the black shale ironstone, 23 yards above the coal was opened, and has since been regularly worked. The extension of the ironstone workings towards the outcrop has let down the surface water more rapidly than the pumps could lift, and consequently, there has been a gradual accumulation in the No. 1 pit workings. At the time of the breach, 11th June 1861, there was 14 yards in depth No. 1 pits, and a head of 24 yards at the breach. [This would not have been known at the time.]

The No. 2 pits were sunk in 1839, under Mr Stephenson's directions, and both shafts were tubbed [lined with either iron or brick]. The main or black shale coal being found free of water in these pits, Mr Stephenson decided to have no communication with No. 1 pits, so as to keep the large feeder of water in those workings.

Section of Blackshale Seam:

Top coal	22 inches
Parting	2 inches
Parting coal	8 inches
Parting	3 inches
Bottom coal	20 inches"

The report carries much the same story as is already told, except that the stone heads, were in fact a heading rising up from the blackshale workings to the Tupton Sea (also known as the Low Main Seam) 60 yards above the blackshale.

After detailing the positions of the bodies, discipline of the mine etc, the report continues:

APPENDIX I

"I made an early examination of the breach [in Dawes' stall], and found a hole 16 inches wide and 8 inches deep in the parting between the top and bottom coal, and in a narrow pointed corner of a heading 4 feet 6 inches through; the heading had been driven from the point C. It is probable that Martin had driven this heading as a lodge for water until he had worked the coal up a short distance, when the goaf [waste] would hold the water that drained from the coal. A small water lodge had been made between B,C, when Mr Binns surveyed this work, which he laid down on the plan. This may have filled, and Martin ordered this heading to be driven for a like purpose. The distance from C,E, is 43 yards.

The 15th general rule provides 'That sufficient bore holes shall be kept in advance, and if necessary on both sides [of a heading advancing], to prevent inundations in every working place approaching a place likely to contain a dangerous accumulation of water'. Mr Binns stated that he had confidence in the accuracy of his plan of No. 1 pits; and having tested the plan of No. 2 pits he felt secure in an approach to No. 1 workings of 40 yards. That he considered it safer without boring and 40 yards barrier, than 20 yards barrier (minimum required) and a series of bore holes.

The danger in approaching old workings is from an isolated head being driven beyond the limits shown in a plan. A series of bore holes may be made without discovering a head driven beyond the main workings. In this case had two holes been bored 15 yards back from the present face of the stalls and bored 20 yards, it is doubtful whether either would have hit this heading.

From this accident we learn two important lessons: firstly that extreme accuracy is necessary in laying down upon a plan every detail of the workings of a mine; and secondly, the necessity, where two shafts are upon or near the same level, in inclined seams, of an outlet on the rise, or communications with the workings on the rise side of the shafts, and the shafts some distance above the bottom, as a means of escape. If the latter is done it will be a far greater protection in case of inundation of water than boring. There have been several instances of bore holes failing to discover casual headings in old drowned workings. Hence the necessity of means of escape on the rise of the shafts. For several years the plans of Clay Cross have been kept with accuracy. A surveyor is employed solely in the colliery, who records upon the plans every detail. The underviewers give notice when any work is opened, and it is immediately surveyed and recorded. I had opportunities of testing the accuracy of these plans during the recovery of the bodies.

It is gratifying to know that the 14 widows and 32 children of the sufferers have been comfortably provided for. Ten of the children can earn their own living. Mr Jackson, on behalf of the Clay Cross Company, offered to make provision for the bereaved. Many gentlemen of the county expressed a desire to show their respect for the firm and Mr Binns by being allowed to subscribe to a fund for the support of the widows and children. A fund of £2,000 was raised, headed with £500 from the firm. This amount is considered more than sufficient for the purpose. A widow without children is allowed from 8 shillings to 9 shillings per week, and coals; a widow with children, from 12 shillings to 14 shillings per week, and coals [there were 20 shillings to the pound]."

The inspector, Mr Hedley's reasoning on the merits and demerits of boring to prove old underground workings is well and good, plausible, and cannot be faulted, but bearing in mind the fact that a large reservoir of hidden water was to be expected (irrespective of whether the five stalls were marked on the plan or not), it is a little strange that he did not inject a word of censure at least, but then, he had been consulted about the barrier, and the company were noted for keeping accurate plans!

Before finally closing the pages of Mr Hedley's report, a few of his other cases for 1861 are worth noting. They show very well the attitude of the men towards danger, the complete lack of even basic medical care, and the very real danger of life underground.

No. 23 accident

The deceased went into a heading to fill coals, when he lighted a small accumulation of gas, which had gathered during an hour after the header had left. The heading being unventilated, I was authorised by you to prosecute the owner for breach of general rule 1. The deceased was only slightly burned. It was stated at the inquest that his death had been hastened by drinking an embrocation of oil and turpentine, instead of applying it to the burns.

No. 27 accident

The deceased passed a fire board (danger signal) with a lighted candle. He had been ordered out of the stall; but returned again unknown to anyone.

No. 28 accident

The deceased was passing through the main separation doors near the shaft, when he ignited a small quantity of gas. He was only slightly burned; but being in a bad state of body, he died of shock. All the above accidents were by explosion.

No. 8 accident

The cage was descending when deceased attempted to run through the pit bottom, the cage dropped upon him. There was a road around the shaft.

No. 10 accident

Deceased, contrary to the special rules, and also the advice of those near him, was holing without sprags set to keep up the coal.

No. 26 accident

Owing to an accident to the fencing at the pit top it was removed. A stop catch was fixed to the rails to prevent the trams being pushed into the shaft. It was the duty of the deceased to put down the catch before he took a tram to the pit top. He omitted this, and was pushing the tram towards the shaft with his head down; the tram fell into the shaft and dragged him with it. [This accident was at the Speedwell pit, Staveley.]

The Ilkeston (Derbyshire) Permanent Rescue Brigade 1919. Note the heavy apparatus, horns for communicating simple commands, 'bulls eyes' electric hand lamps and two canaries. Compare this 'luxury' with the illustration of rescuers descending the shaft in the bucket.

Appendix II

THE COAL MINES ACT

In order that the reader may briefly trace the road along which mining legislation had travelled up to the passing of the Coal Mines Act, 1911, this short summary may be useful. All the events in this story happened before the Act came into operation on the 1st July 1912, and there is no need to list further subsequent legislation here. The student of mining history will find ample lists of the full provisions, amendment and repeals in the Mines and Quarries Act, 1954, 2 & 3 Eliz 2.

This Appendix has been extracted from articles written by William Straker and first published in the *Newcastle Daily Chronicle* in June 1912, and subsequently in the Northumberland Miners' Mutual Confident Association's publication of the full text of the 1911 Act.

The Act of 1911 came into being as the latest in a series of such Acts passed for the greater safety of mine workers. Like its predecessors, it owed much of its character to terrible mine disasters which drew public attention to the need for provisions better calculated to prevent such calamities. This Act was very important as it seemed that for the first time, the question of cost had not been allowed to stand in the way of provisions to secure greater safety for life and limb. The Members of Parliament, other than those with vested interests in mining, had little patience with any plea of costs advanced against its proposal, a terrible series of major disasters just before the introduction of the Act would seem to have been the final straw.

Early Legislation
There are many instances, which are mentioned in legislative records, of the granting of rights to work coal in the county of Derby from the 13th century onwards. In the 16th century coal exports were the attention of national leaders, concerned that only inferior sorts should be sent abroad and the best retained at home. In 1563 Scotland passed an Act that no one should: "na tak onie coale be shippe". Fifteen years later James VI confirmed this Act and eighteen years later still, passed another statute which ordered the bodies of those that would "tak grit coale out o the kingdom" to be taken care of − a suggestive way of putting it, which doubtless was well understood in its day.

In 1606 another Act took care of the bodies of the colliers. It enacted that if the "saide coalyiers, do leave their maisters without consent, they are to be esteemed report and houlden as thieves of themselves of cowrse for leaving such maisters". It also gave permission to the "maisters" and owners to lay hold of all vagabonds and sturdy beggars, and compel them to work in the pits. By this time Elizabeth of England had also imposed a duty of five shillings per chaldron on all coal exported by sea (a chaldron was equivalent to approximately 53 cwt).

In the year 1661 just after Charles II came to the throne, an Act was passed against the idleness of the pitmen, and also against giving them too high wages. This was not a 'minimum' but a 'maximum' wage Act. It enacted that the pitmen had to work "all the six days in the week, because not working constantly is a great offence to God, and to the prejudice of the maisters". If the pitmen violated this law they were to pay certain fines, and, if need be, suffer other punishment in "their bodies". It was not until the last year of the 18th century that pitmen were liberated from this condition of slavery.

Women in the Mines
Before 1842 females of all ages, able to work at all, were employed underground in many districts of Scotland and England. Lord Ashley's enquiry led to the passing of the 1842 Mines Act, which prohibited females from working underground. It also prohibited boys from working in the mine before they were 10 years of age.

Nineteenth Century Death Rolls
In June 1835, a Select Committee of the House of Commons was appointed "to enquire into the nature, cause and extent of those lamentable catastrophies which have occurred in the mines of Great Britain. With a view of ascertaining and suggesting the means for preventing the recurrence of similar fatal accidents." The miners themselves agitated in the matter, until in 1850 the first Mines Inspection Act was passed. It was a meagre and experimental measure, and limited to five years. However, the miners, once aroused, could not be satisfied with a terminable measure such as this, so at the end of the five years another Act was passed. Both these Acts served to show that much more could be done, consequently the agitation was kept up, and in the year 1860 another Act was placed on the statute book, which, unlike its two predecessors, was not limited to any period. Twelve years afterwards, 1872, an Act was passed "to consolidate and amend the Acts relating to the regulation of coal mines and certain other mines". This was far more wide-reaching than the 1860 Act, yet it was far from meeting the demands of those interested in the safety of mining.

The 1887 Act
In 1887 the Act was passed which, with some amendments, remained in operation until July 1912, and which from the workmen's point of view was a great advance on the Act of 1872. The power of "a Secretary of State" to grant liberty to the owners of certain pits to employ underground boys under 12 years of age was taken away. Weighing of the produce of the coal hewers was made compulsory, except at mines employing underground not more than 30 persons. Under the 1872 Act the person appointed as check-weigher by the workmen had to be an employee of the owner of the colliery. There were other restrictions which in effect enabled the colliery owner to veto the choice of the workmen when appointing a check-weigher, the Act of 1887 practically gave the men a free hand to appoint anyone they desired.

Many of the general rules were improved, especially those relating to 'daily supervision', use of safety lamps and explosives. It was also made compulsory for the mine owner to provide suitable timber in men's places or in a convenient position. The 1887 Act made it compulsory for every mine to be under a first-class certificated manager responsible for the control, management and direction of the mine. It also provided for daily supervision of the mine, but allowed this to be done by an undermanager possessing only a second-class certificate. Under these provisions one manager might be placed over a large group of mines, and know practically nothing of the underground conditions of any of them other than from the reports of his under-official. The separate mines were thus for practical purposes under the management of a second-class certificated person, which was clearly against the intention, if not the letter, of the Act. At the Hulton pits in Lancashire, when a terrible explosion occurred in 1910, the manager had nine pits under his control, which made it impossible for him to have intimate knowledge of any of them.

The differences between the provisions made in the Acts of 1887 and 1911 need to be studied in greater depth than can be included here. In general terms, the latter dotted the i's and crossed the t's which the earlier Act had failed to notice. Supervision, Certificates of Competency, firemen, examiners and deputies' appointments were all tightened. Consider the following statement in the second report of the Royal Commission on Mines as to the inability of many colliery officials to test for inflammable gas: "In some mines as little as one per cent, was not only detected and reported, but regarded with anxiety by the officials. In other mines the officials not only failed to detect far higher proportions but were totally ignorant of how to test for anything short of an explosive mixture." With this state of things, one ceases to wonder at explosions.

The 1887 Act required that "no lamp or light other than a locked safety lamp shall be allowed or used" when there was likely to be such quantity of inflammable gas as to render the use of naked lights dangerous. This was so indefinite that any quantity of gas might be present before it was declared dangerous. (The main argument about the relative merits of the safety lamp and the candle is discussed in this story, see page 103.)

Workmen's inspection, official reports, ventilation, winding apparatus, roof and side support and the growing use of electricity all claimed special attention in the 1911 Act, and nothing more drastic had been done in mining legislation since it was made compulsory to have two shafts at every mine than the provisions in the new Act for separate travelling and haulage roads.

In conclusion, the miners of Great Britain had cause to welcome the Coal Mines Act 1911, it had been a bitter struggle to get that far, even reading this all too brief review it must be obvious what conditions generally were like before 1887. Bearing in mind lessons learned in the 20th century, perhaps the final word on the Act should be left to William Straker: "I have been anxious to enable miners to partly grasp the importance of what has been accomplished by those who have acted on their behalf. I have no desire to make anyone believe that all is now done that can or ought to be done in the shape of mining legislation, but it is only by fully understanding and appreciating that which has been done that we can hope to see more accomplished."

GLOSSARY

Adit A more or less horizontal entrance to a mine.

Afterdamp The mixture of gases in a mine after an explosion, mainly carbon monoxide.

Back shift The afternoon or night shift.

Bank (1) Hill or brow. (2) The actual coal face, *see also* Benk. *See also* Brought to bank.

Banksman The person in charge of the shaft and cages at the surface of a colliery; the person at the surface who operates the signals to the winding engine and the pit bottom.

Bassett (1) An outcrop of a seam or strata. (2) Bassett pit: a shaft close to the outcrop of a seam.

Bat Shale or stone in coal.

Benk The same as Bank (2), a Derbyshire expression for coal face.

Blackdamp A gas which puts out flame lamps; also known as chokedamp or stythe, mainly carbon dioxide.

Blow To fire shots; also said of a floor which lifts due to pressure of gas or strata.

Blower Gas under pressure escaping from floor or face.

Bord The main cleavage in coal seams; the direction of that cleat.

Brattice A ventilation partition.

Brattice cloth Cloth used for brattices or doors.

Brought to bank Brought out of the mine.

Bucket Hoppit (local term) used by sinkers and formerly used before cages.

Buttock A corner formed by two faces at right angles to each other.

Butty A mate or partner.

Butty man A man in charge of others who was paid for the whole job and pays those under him; in Derbyshire, a contractor.

Chokedamp See Blackdamp.

Cleat Cleavage Planes more or less at right angles to the roof and floor along which the coal tends to split readily. They are called 'bord' as regards the main cleavage, and 'end' as regards secondary planes.

Collier An experienced coal-getter.

Corporal A chargehand below the rank of Deputy, in charge of workers. (Had wider powers in the 19th century.)

Cross-cut A road connecting two other more important roads.

Cross-gate A road driven at about 45° to the main roads; a slantgate.

Cross measures A road which is driven from one seam to another, or which intersects a number of seams; a drift.

Darley Abbey An abbey near Derby, had extensive land-holdings in Derbyshire during the Middle Ages.

Deep The side which is dipping away and downhill.

Deputy Responsible examiner – the statutory official in charge of a district underground.

Dip To incline downhill; the full inclination; true dip is the fullest inclination of a strata.

Dirt Anything solid other than wood or coal.

Drift A road driven in solid ground, but not in coal. A mine entrance driven from the surface.

Dumb drift Short inclined flue driven from a furnace to the shaft.

Empty An empty tub or waggon.

GLOSSARY

End Secondary cleavage at right angles to Bord or Face.

Face The actual coal wall where the coal is being got.

Firedamp Inflammable gas, mainly methane.

Forest In Derbyshire in the Middle Ages, much land was described as forest. In reading old documents, care must be taken not to confuse words like 'collier' or 'collyer' with charcoal-burners.

Gannister Hard siliceous sandstone.

Gas Firedamp.

Gate Underground road, usually leading to an actual working face, main-gate, tail-gate. In old documents: *Gata* . . . the road or way to somewhere.

Gin Old form of winding apparatus, mainly horse powered.

Goaf Waste after the coal has been extracted; Gob, Waste.

Grit Coarse grained sandstone.

Headgear The headframe of a mine.

Heading A new or exploring road into solid strata, or a development road in a seam.

Holing Undercutting a seam to free the coal, 'holing out'.

Hoppit A bucket, kibble, used in shafts before cages, which were usually termed chairs.

Ignition An outburst of fire or explosion.

Ironstone Argillaceous ore of iron found in coal measures.

Motty Check, tally or token.

Onsetter The person in charge of winding operations from underground, gives all signals to the winding engineman.

Overman A mine official between Deputy and Undermanager.

Pack A form of permanent roof support built from waste; does not give immediate support, but takes the weight gradually as the roof settles.

Putter One who hauls tubs by hand, usually a teenager.

Riders Men ascending or descending a shaft. A special signal is given to warn the engineman. In former days the banksman would cry down the shaft: "Riders a-coming".

Rise Incline uphill; a road inclined uphill.

Roadlaying Laying track for transport.

Round coal Large lumps free from dirt or smalls.

Slit A connecting road.

Sough Level driven to the lowest point of a 'take' to drain mine water away from the workings.

Split A branching of the ventilating current.

Sprag A short prop either set slantwise or under cut coal for a temporary support.

Stall A working place at the coal face.

Standage A sump or lodge used as a reservoir for water.

Take Area of coal allotted to a mine.

Thirling A connecting road; slit; cross-cut.

Tommy shop Owned by a coal owner or contractor, gave goods at inflated prices on credit. Declared illegal by early legislation, but continued in milder forms in some areas.

Tram A mine tub, small waggon on wheels.

Tubbing Iron or steel segments to support shaft sides against water pressure or unsound ground.

Viewer Originally a mining engineer with the 'view' of a number of collieries. Headviewer, underviewer were variations. The modern undermanager has little in common with the term.

Waste The area behind an advancing coal face from which the coal has been removed, the props withdrawn and the roof allowed to collapse.

Weight Downward pressure of the superincumbent strata above a coal face, roof movement, especially when it can be heard or seen.

Whitedamp Carbon monoxide, a gas associated with white fumes.

Windroad Airway or air road; ventilation road.